NATURAL ENVIRONMENT RES
INSTITUTE OF TER

WOODLICE IN BRITAIN AND IRELAND: DISTRIBUTION AND HABITAT

Compiled and edited
for the
British Isopoda Study Group

by

Paul T Harding
(Institute of Terrestrial Ecology)

and

Stephen L Sutton
(University of Leeds)

Biological Records Centre
Institute of Terrestrial Ecology
Monks Wood Experimental Station
Abbots Ripton
Huntingdon

Dedication

To Alan Cadogan, Eric Duffey, Charles Elton and Kitty Southern who independently fostered our interest in woodlice; and also to Philippa Harding, Stephanie Sutton and our respective families who have put up with the consequences for so many years.

Contents

Figures

Tables

Foreword

Whether or not woodlice have a particular fascination for you, you are almost bound to come across them in any branch of field biology. At times I have met them as the prey of the spider *Dysdera crocata*, a predator with long thin chelicerae and long fine fangs adapted to seizing and piercing their prey, the woodlice (there is an excellent illustration of the capture of a woodlouse by one of these spiders on page 97 of W S Bristowe's *The world of spiders*, Collins New Naturalist series). On another occasion I remember the thrill, when looking in an ants' nest in the Yorkshire Wolds, of seeing for the first time the weird white woodlouse, *Platyarthrus hoffmannseggi*, walking unconcernedly amongst the ants, and, with casual inspection only, looking rather like a large larva or pupa (there is a superb coloured illustration of this woodlouse in S L Sutton's *Woodlice*, Ginn). Woodlice, as one can see, have a habit of walking into almost any branch of natural history, and hence I hope that this "atlas" will have a wide use amongst many naturalists.

The book is in 2 parts, as indicated by the title; a book of maps would be a reference work only, whereas a book of words has a wider usage. I shall turn to the maps in a moment, but the words describe what is currently known about the woodlice of Great Britain and Ireland. As usual with a group of animals, a reasonable amount is known about a few species and rather little is known about a lot of species. The authors allow themselves to do a spot of speculation, as with the distribution of *Porcellionides cingendus:* I hope that such speculation kindles enough controversy amongst other naturalists that it will provide the impetus for more to be found out about the biology of many of these animals.

It is a particular feature of the British Isles that everything, or almost everything, is mapped. This is not only an academic exercise, since the maps provide the data that both practical naturalists and theoretical ecologists will use. Where to look for a particular species, or which "under-recorded squares" to visit (the occupation for the real enthusiast who wants to add a few more dots), are both examples of the use of an atlas such as this by naturalists. The more theoretical ecologist can count the squares, and measure areas, to establish species-area relationships, can undertake computer analyses to see if there are good biological bases for regionalization of the country, or can investigate the correlations between pairs of species or between a species and aspects of the environment.

As well as the future use of a work of this nature, one should also think of the past, since the task of compilation has taken many years, involving many amateurs and professionals alike in searching, identifying, recording, and broadening our knowledge of the British fauna. The project has resulted in much new knowledge being gained, including the discovery of one species of woodlouse new to science *(Metatrichoniscoides celticus)* and 3 species previously unknown in the British Isles (see Appendix 2 for details).

However, the success of this book is not just measured by how many people use it, but also by how much stimulation it provides for gathering new information. In wishing the compilers and editors well, I trust that their *Woodlice in Britain and Ireland: distribution and habitat* is out of date very quickly, and that they will soon be writing the second edition.

Michael B Usher

Preface

This volume is an attempt to summarize information gathered in the 16 years since the inception of the Isopod Survey Scheme in 1968. Unlike other biological recording schemes being set up at that time, we were interested in collecting habitat data as well as mapping distributions. In this way, we hoped to produce interpretative texts alongside our maps. The *Provisional atlas* (Harding 1976a) followed this approach in a modest way, but it was not until the latest analysis of the many thousands of record cards was completed in January 1983 that the present treatment became possible.

The maps in this volume occupy less than one third of the pages, which is why we have avoided the term 'Atlas' in the title, preferring instead to emphasize the interpretation of distribution in relation to habitat as our basic aim in this work.

The Isopod Survey Scheme was born out of ignorance—both of the detailed distribution of woodlice in the British Isles and of the amount of work involved in trying to overcome this deficiency. The extent to which the effort has been worthwhile we must leave to others to judge, but we can note with satisfaction that the survey has given us the opportunity to work with an exceptional band of able and dedicated people. The recorders, some of whom contributed to this volume, scoured the landscape with prodigious energy, leaving, dare we say it, almost no stone unturned in their search for the inevitable *Oniscus asellus*. It will always be a privilege to work with such people. A full list of recorders is given in Appendix I.

We are very grateful to the following who contributed to the species accounts in Section IV:

A O Chater (British Museum (Natural History))
Dr G M Collis (University of Strathclyde)
Mrs P J Copson (Warwick Museum)
D Doogue (Irish Biogeographical Society)
G D Fussey (University of Leeds/Eton College)
Dr A G Irwin (Castle Museum, Norwich)
Dr P G Oliver (National Museum of Wales)
D T Richardson (Yorkshire Naturalists' Union)
Miss A Trew (National Museum of Wales)
R Willows (University of Leeds)

We would also like to thank Declan Doogue for regional organization in Ireland, and Glyn and Dawn Collis for the same in Scotland. We are grateful to Dr Colin Fairhurst (Salford University) for developing techniques for computer analysis of our data and making the early analyses, and to Dr Graham Oliver for contributing Appendix 2, the text figures in Section V and early drafts of some coastal habitat accounts. We are also grateful to IBM and the John Spedan Lewis Trust for providing small grants when the survey was started, and to the World Wildlife Fund (British National Appeal) for funding the special survey of *Halophiloscia couchi* sites in 1973.

We would also like to thank Mrs D M Greene, Mrs D W Awdry, Mrs C Binge and Mrs S D Pauley of the Institute of Terrestrial Ecology; G J Moller and Mrs L Ling of the NERC Computing Services for data processing; and Mrs S M Weller and Miss J M Abblitt of ITE for typing.

Paul T Harding

Stephen L Sutton

I. INTRODUCTION

The heart of this book is a series of accounts of individual species, detailing the frequency with which each has been recorded from particular habitats and microsites during the course of the Isopod Survey Scheme. These data are presented in a standard format to aid comparisons between species. A map including all verified records, up to the end of August 1982, faces the text for each species. The contributors and the editors have tried to draw out, from the survey, tentative statements concerning the status and ecological requirements of each species in the British Isles.

References to the published literature are included to link with detailed studies of particular species.

The opportunity has also been taken to look at the distribution and abundance of woodlice, habitat by habitat, with particular emphasis on specialized coastal habitats, where several recently discovered and little known species are found. The detailed description of these sites should aid further study of their special woodlouse fauna. To underpin these sections, a definitive checklist of British species is given, together with details of the higher classification of these species and the key works available for their identification.

The various stages in the development of the Isopod Survey Scheme are outlined, from its origin in 1968. Here, the collection, validation and processing of material and data are also summarized. A discussion of the strengths and weaknesses of the habitat classification, in the light of experience, is included.

There are 6 Appendices. The first gives a list of all those who recorded for the Isopod Survey Scheme and the second gives descriptions and figures of 4 species new to the British Isles list since Sutton (1972), including *Metatrichoniscoides celticus*, described as a species new to science by Oliver and Trew (1981). Accounts of *Miktoniscus patiencei* and *Buddelundiella cataractae* have been published elsewhere, but the present account of *Stenophiloscia zosterae* is the first based on British material.

Appendix 3 summarizes the dubious claims of *Trachelipus ratzeburgi* to a place in the list of species recorded from the British Isles, to justify its exclusion from the checklist in Section II. Appendix 4 is a facsimile of the *Instructions to collectors* and Appendix 5 gives a list of the total number and percentage of records made in each habitat. Details of the abundance of species in each habitat (as the percentage of total records for each habitat attributable to each species) are available on request, but the table is too bulky to publish. Readers may also wish to note that copies of the Isopod Survey Scheme newsletters are also available on request from the Biological

Records Centre. Appendix 6 provides lists of the species whose survival in the British Isles is considered to be under threat.

A major aim in the publication of this volume is to make effective use of the data-collecting power available through the spare-time activity of our group of recorders. Such a means of data collection would not be cost effective as a full-time research project, but, in our view, it has a most valuable part to play in creating a broad background of knowledge which allows narrow-based projects (confined to one site or one species, for example) to be pursued with greater success. We hope that the links between our extensive survey and intensive research projects will prove fruitful, and that each kind of project will stimulate the other.

The publication of this volume is timely in that it coincides in late 1984 with the appearance of Volume 53 of the Symposium series of the Zoological Society of London, which has the title *The biology of terrestrial isopods* (Sutton & Holdich 1984). This volume contains a number of papers which are relevant to the distributions and habitats of British species, including:

FEDERICI, B. A. Diseases of terrestrial isopods.
HASSALL, M. & RUSHTON, S. P. Feeding behaviour of terrestrial isopods in relation to plant defences and microbial activity.
SCHMALFUSS, H. Eco-morphological strategies in terrestrial isopods.
SUTTON, S. L., HASSALL, M., WILLOWS, R., DAVIS, R. C., GRUNDY, A. & SUNDERLAND, K. D. Life histories of terrestrial isopods: a study of intra- and interspecific variation.
WARBURG, M. H., LINSENMAIR, K. E. & BERCOVITZ, K. Oniscid distribution and abundance.
WIESER, W. Ecophysiological adaptions of terrestrial isopods: a brief review.
WILLOWS, R. Breeding phenology of woodlice and oostegite development of *Ligia oceanica* (L.) (Crustacea: Oniscidea).

The years since the publication of Sutton (1972), when the literature was last summarized, have seen an increasing number of papers on the ecology of woodlice, apart from those in the Symposium volume mentioned above. Standen (1973) described the life history and annual production of *Trichoniscus pusillus* in a Cheshire wood, work which forms an interesting parallel with Sutton (1968) and Phillipson (1983) working on *T. pusillus* in Wytham Woods, Berkshire. In 1976, Lawlor produced 2 important papers on reproductive strategies in *Armadillidium vulgare*.

McQueen (1976) (and previous papers) discussed climate and the demography of *Trachelipus rathkei*. Frankel (1979a) completed a series of papers on the reproductive biology and growth of *Trichoniscus pusillus* and Sutton and Coghill (1979) summarized the status of woodlice as pests. Al-Dabbagh and

Block (1981) gave details of an intensive study of *Armadillidium vulgare* at 2 contrasting sites in Norfolk and Suffolk. Fussey (1984) examined the distribution of the diploid and triploid forms of *Trichoniscus pusillus* in the British Isles.

Long-term studies of the ecology of *Armadillidium vulgare, Philoscia muscorum* and *Porcellio scaber* at Spurn Head, South-east Yorkshire, in progress since 1968, have led to 14 theses and publications to date. These are reviewed by Sutton *et al.* (1984). Among them are: Sunderland, Hassall and Sutton (1976), Hassall and Sutton (1978), Sunderland and Sutton (1980), and Davis (1984).

All the above papers take a specialist approach. The only general introduction to woodlice in print is Sutton (1980). This is a re-publication, without alteration, of Sutton (1972), by Pergamon Press of Oxford. It describes the basic morphology, behaviour and ecology of the group.

II CHECKLIST, NOMENCLATURE AND KEY WORKS

Checklist and Nomenclature

The British Isles checklist was last revised by Sutton, Harding and Burn (1972), although Doogue and Harding (1982) added to Sutton's list 4 species recorded new to the British Isles since 1972 *(Buddelundiella cataractae, Metatrichoniscoides celticus, Miktoniscus patiencei* and *Stenophiloscia zosterae* (Appendix 2)). The classification of Crustacea (Bowman & Abele 1982), and of woodlice in particular (Holdich, Lincoln & Ellis 1984), has received attention recently.

This checklist follows the sequence proposed by Holdich *et al.* for the Suborder Oniscidea, down to family. Within each section and superfamily, Holdich *et al.* placed families in alphabetical sequence because the phylogenetic relationships of the Suborder are poorly understood. Following this precedent, the genera within families and the species within genera are listed in an alphabetical sequence, rather than in a supposed phylogenetic sequence.

Currently accepted nomenclature is used throughout this volume. In the checklist any synonyms used in publication, relating to species in Britain or Ireland, are listed beneath the current name. Alien species (see below) are indicated with an asterisk. All other species are considered to be native or naturalized.

Suborder *Oniscidea*

Section *Diplocheta*

Family *Ligiidae*

Ligia oceanica (Linnaeus, 1767)
Ligia scopulorum Leach, 1810
Ligidium hypnorum (Cuvier, 1792)
Ligidium agile (Persoon, 1793)
Zia saundersii Stebbing, 1873

Section *Synocheta*

Superfamily *Trichoniscoidea*

Family *Trichoniscidae*

Androniscus dentiger Verhoeff, 1908
Philougria rosea sensu auct. Brit, not C. L. Koch, 1837
Trichoniscus roseus sensu auct. Brit, not C. L. Koch, 1837
Androniscus weberi Verhoeff, 1908
Stenasellus hazeltoni Collinge, 1946
Buddelundiella cataractae Verhoeff, 1930

Haplophthalmus danicus Budde-Lund, 1880
Haplophthalmus mengei (Zaddach, 1844)
Metatrichoniscoides celticus Oliver & Trew, 1981
**Miktoniscus linearis* (Patience, 1908)
Trichoniscus linearis Patience, 1908
Miktoniscus patiencei Vandel, 1946
Oritoniscus flavus (Budde-Lund, 1906)
Philougria vivida sensu auct. Brit, not C. L. Koch, 1841
Trichoniscus vividus sensu auct. Brit, not C. L. Koch, 1841
Trichoniscus vandelius Collinge, 1945
Trichoniscoides albidus (Budde-Lund, 1880)
Trichoniscoides saeroeensis Lohmander, 1923
Trichoniscoides sarsi Patience, 1908
Trichoniscus pusillus Brandt, 1833
Philougria celer Kinahan, 1857
Philougria riparia sensu auct. Brit, not C. L. Koch, 1835
Trichoniscus pygmaeus Sars, 1899

Superfamily *Styloniscoidea*

Family *Styloniscidae*

**Cordioniscus stebbingi* (Patience, 1907)
Trichoniscus stebbingi Patience, 1907
**Styloniscus spinosus* (Patience, 1907)
Trichoniscus spinosus Patience, 1907
Cordioniscus spinosus (Patience, 1907)

Section *Crinocheta*

Superfamily *Oniscoidea*

Family *Halophilosciidae*

Halophiloscia couchi (Kinahan, 1858)
Philoscia couchii Kinahan, 1858
Stenophiloscia zosterae Verhoeff, 1928
Halophiloscia (Stenophiloscia) zosterae Verhoeff, 1928

Family *Oniscidae*

Oniscus asellus Linnaeus, 1758
Oniscus murarius Cuvier, 1792
Oniscus fossor C. L. Koch, 1838

Family *Philosciidae*

**Chaetophiloscia meeusei* Holthuis, 1947
**Chaetophiloscia patiencei* (Bagnall, 1908)
Philoscia patiencei Bagnall, 1908
Philoscia muscorum (Scopoli 1763)

Family *Platyarthridae*

Platyarthrus hoffmannseggi Brandt, 1833
**Trichorhina tomentosa* (Budde-Lund, 1893)

Superfamily *Porcellionoidea*

Family *Armadillidiidae*

Armadillidium album Dollfus, 1887
Armadillidium depressum Brandt, 1833
Armadillidium nasatum Budde-Lund, 1885
 Armadillidium speyeri Jackson, 1923
Armadillidium pictum Brandt, 1833
Armadillidium pulchellum (Zenker, 1798)
Armadillidium vulgare (Latreille, 1804)
 Armadillo vulgaris (Latreille, 1804)
 Armadillium vulgare (Latreille, 1804)
 Armadillidium cinereum sensu auct. Brit. not (Zenker, 1793)
Eluma purpurascens Budde-Lund, 1885

Family *Cubaridae*

**Reductoniscus costulatus* Kessleyák, 1930

Family *Cylisticidae*

Cylisticus convexus (De Geer, 1778)
 Porcellio armadilloides (Lereboullet, 1853)

Family *Porcellionidae*

Acaeroplastes melanurus (Budde-Lund, 1885)
 Metoponorthus melanurus Budde-Lund, 1885
 Porcellionides melanurus (Budde-Lund, 1885)
**Agabiformius lentus* (Budde-Lund, 1885)
 Angara lenta Budde-Lund, 1909
Porcellio dilatatus Brandt, 1833
Porcellio laevis Latreille, 1804
Porcellio scaber Latreille, 1804
Porcellio spinicornis Say, 1818
 Porcellio pictus Brandt & Ratzeburg, 1833
Porcellionides cingendus (Kinahan, 1857)
 Porcellio cingendus Kinahan, 1857
 Metoponorthus cingendus (Kinahan, 1857)
Porcellionides pruinosus (Brandt, 1833)
 Porcellio pruinosus Brandt, 1833
 Metoponorthus pruinosus (Brandt, 1833)

Family *Trachelipidae*

**Nagurus cristatus* (Dollfus, 1881)

**Nagurus nanus* Budde-Lund, 1908
Nagara nana Budde-Lund, 1908
Trachelipus rathkei (Brandt, 1833)
Porcellio rathkei Brandt, 1833

Extinct species

One species, *Acaeroplastes melanurus*, is believed to be extinct. It was known from only one area, the southern cliffs of Howth, Co. Dublin, where it was recorded on several occasions between 1909 and 1934. Repeated searches of the area since 1972 have failed to record it (Doogue & Harding 1982).

Alien species

This volume does not concern itself with the many alien species recorded at some time from the British Isles. The occurrence of such species is unpredictable, with the largest number of species having been recorded in glasshouses at botanic gardens, such as those at Kew, Cambridge, Glasgow, Dublin and Belfast. A few species have been recorded in commercial glasshouses and in garden centres. Almost all these species are apparently of tropical or sub-tropical origin and many are now known to be widespread in Europe, in heated glasshouses, particularly in botanic gardens. Of the 10 alien species listed above, 4 have not been recorded during the period of the survey. Several additional species (including some collected by R S Bagnall at Kew, before 1921 (Ellis & Lincoln 1975)) remain unidentified. *Chaetophiloscia meeusei*, described as new to science from Kew (Holthuis 1947), has not been recorded in the wild and is therefore known only as an alien species, from one glasshouse range at Kew.

Key works

Although early accounts of the woodlice of the British Isles are of considerable interest in tracing the development of the study of this group, the major publications (Bate & Westwood 1868; Scharff 1894; Norman 1899, 1903; Webb & Sillem 1906; Pack Beresford & Foster 1911) are not useful for the identification of specimens. It is perhaps fortunate that W E Collinge's *Introduction to the terrestrial Isopoda (woodlice) of the British Isles* remained unpublished at his death in 1947, because of the unreliable nature of the keys and identification features used (Harding 1977).

The basic keys to most species occurring in the British Isles are those by Edney (1953, 1954). The keys produced by Sutton *et al.* (1972) and published in Sutton (1972, 1980) were intended to complement, rather than to replace, Edney's keys. Two continental works (Vandel 1960a, 1962; Gruner 1966) have proved essential for the additional information they provide in species descriptions, and on distribution and ecology.

III. **RECORDING**

A. Historical background and development of the survey

The original idea for a survey of the distributions and habitats of isopods in the British Isles was conceived by S L Sutton and R J A Metcalfe on a cold evening in January 1968, in Cambridge, following a meeting of the British Ecological Society. The species mapping schemes, pioneered in 1954 for vascular plants by the Botanical Society of the British Isles, and in 1967 for macro-Lepidoptera by the Biological Records Centre (BRC), acted as a blueprint for the survey of isopods, but were considered by Sutton and Metcalfe as somewhat limited in their objectives. They planned to expand the concept of species mapping to include a survey of the habitats of species.

A recording card (Figure 1) was printed which listed most of the terrestrial and freshwater species and a selection of marine species, with an appropriate list of habitats. The Isopod Survey Scheme was launched in December 1968. By this time, P T Harding, who had been reviewing the vice-county distribution of woodlice, had joined Sutton and Metcalfe to help organize the survey. Newsletter no. 1 of the survey was produced in March 1969.

In 1969, BRC had been considering a mapping scheme to cover woodlice, millipedes and centipedes, and had approached a specialist in myriapods to organize it. Discussions in 1969 between BRC, Sutton, Metcalfe and Harding, and 2 myriapodologists, C P Fairhurst and A D Barber, reached agreement that interrelated surveys of woodlice, millipedes and centipedes should be set up under the aegis of BRC. Sutton and Metcalfe's original concept of habitat recording was extended and developed as a hierarchical habitat classification, specifically designed for these taxonomic groups, by D M Burn, Sutton and Fairhurst. A draft classification was given extensive field trials at the meeting of the newly formed British Myriapod Group, in Easter 1970. Modifications resulted from these field trials, and from further discussions, and a habitat classification for all 3 groups was agreed in May 1970. Recording cards for all 3 groups were printed by BRC later that year (Figure 2).

The original Isopod Survey Scheme included freshwater and marine species. With the development of integrated recording cards for woodlice, millipedes and centipedes, it was decided that marine species should be dealt with separately. D M Holdich (later joined by R J Lincoln) set up a scheme to record marine isopods, with a specially designed hierarchical habitat recording card, in 1972 (Holdich & Lincoln 1974). The 4 species of freshwater isopods were added to the draft card for woodlice, and the habitat classification modified accordingly.

The British Isopod Study Group was formed in 1969 to act as a parent body to the survey. Small grants were obtained from IBM and the John Spedan Lewis Trust which provided working capital to print instructions for the recording card and newsletters.

The organization of the survey was undertaken by Sutton and Metcalfe until 1972, when Harding took over responsibility for the non-marine scheme and Holdich for the marine scheme. The organization of the non-marine scheme was written into the Institute of Terrestrial Ecology's project no. 406, 'Distribution and ecology of non-marine Isopoda', approved in June 1975. Harding continued to organize the non-marine scheme as part of this project until the scheme ended in August 1982. A modified recording scheme has been run since September 1982 by G D Fussey. The marine scheme is now run by Lincoln.

Newsletters have been distributed free to recorders since the survey was launched. They were seen as an essential means of keeping recorders informed of progress, providing useful hints on techniques for finding some of the more elusive species, and giving advice on identification.

Several field meetings have been organized at which both established and novice recorders met and exchanged information, and gathered valuable field experience of species which were often new to them. Meetings were held at Monks Wood (September 1973), Manchester (April 1976), Roscrea, Co. Tipperary (October 1976), Monks Wood (October 1979), Robin Hood's Bay (April 1981) and Cardiff (April 1982). Many local meetings, designed to help inexperienced recorders, have been organized by D Doogue, G M and V D Collis, D T Richardson and A J Rundle.

A *Provisional atlas* was prepared in 1976 (Harding 1976a), summarizing records from 1675 10 km squares. The maps for that atlas were prepared by hand by the editor. No attempt was made to analyse the habitat data, but information on habitats was summarized in brief commentaries on each map. Some of these commentaries now seem embarrassingly inadequate in the light of present knowledge, and 4 species have been added to the British Isles list since its publication (see Section II and Appendix 2). A preliminary review of records of *Asellus* species (freshwater species) was prepared in 1981 (Moon & Harding 1981). A distribution atlas of woodlice in Ireland (Doogue & Harding 1982) summarized almost all the Irish records used in the present volume and included accounts of each species. Only a partial analysis of habitat data was available for use in compiling the species accounts in the Irish atlas.

Recent work has concentrated on improving the overall coverage of the British Isles (inevitably still incomplete) and carrying out the basic analysis of the habitat data to provide the summaries given in this volume. The habitat

LOCALITY

COLL.

DET.

0008 Acaeroplastes melanurus
0010 Androniscus dentiger
0012 weberi
0014 Armadillidium album
0016 depressum
0018 nasatum
0020 opacum
0022 pictum
0024 pulchellum
0026 vulgare
0028 Asellus aquaticus
0030 cavaticus
0032 meridianus
0034 Chaetophiloscia patiencei
0036 Cirolana cranchi
0038 Cordioniscus spinosus
0040 stebbingi
0042 Cylisticus convexus
0044 Eluma purpurascens
0046 Eurydice pulchra
0048 Gnathia maxillaris
0050 Halophiloscia couchi
0052 Haplophthalmus danicus
0054 mengei
0056 Idotea baltica
0058 emarginata
0060 granulosa
0062 linearis
0064 neglecta
0066 pelagica
0068 viridis
0070 Jaera marina
0072 nordmanni
0074 Janira maculosa
0076 Ligia oceanica
0078 Ligidium hypnorum
0080 Limnoria lignorum
0082 Metoponorthus cingendus
0084 pruinosus
0086 Miktoniscus linearis
0088 Munna kroyeri
0090 Naesa bidentata
0092 Oniscus asellus
0094 Oritoniscus flavus
0096 Philoscia muscorum
00961 var. *lutea*
00962 var. *rosea*
0098 Platyarthrus hoffmannseggi
0100 Porcellio (Porcellio) dilatatus
0102 laevis
0104 scaber
0106 spinicornis
0108 (Tracheoniscus) rathkei
0110 ratzeburgi
0112 Sphaeroma rugicauda
0114 serratum
0116 Trichoniscoides albidus
0118 sarsi
0120 Trichoniscus pusillus agg.
01201 *provisorius*
01202 *pusillus*
0122 pygmaeus

Other species:

Trinity and All Saints' Colleges 1968

Figure 1a Original recording card (1968)—front of card

Grid ref.		LOCALITY	
V.C.	V.C.No.	Alt.	Date

MAJOR HABITATS:

Woodland ☐
Scrub ☐
Grass, permanent ☐
Open ground (veg. < 25%) ☐
Heath ☐
Sand dune ☐
Marginal (hedgerows, &c.) ☐
Human habitation ☐
Gardens ☐
Mire ☐
Aquatic ☐
Intertidal ☐
Cave ☐

MINOR HABITATS:

Under stones ☐
Soil ☐
Litter ☐
Garden refuse ☐
Shore-line litter ☐
Dung ☐
Carrion ☐
Dead wood ☐
Bark crevices (living trees) ☐
Moss ☐
Fungi ☐
Nests & burrows ☐
please specify:

Other information
(e.g. vegetation,
source of refuse,
behaviour):

DETAILS OF HABITATS:

Woodland: deciduous ☐
coniferous ☐
mixed ☐
Scrub: > 6ft. ☐
< 6ft. ☐
Grass, perm: > 2ft. ☐
6in. - 2ft. ☐
< 6in. ☐
ungrazed ☐
lightly grazed ☐
heavily grazed ☐
Open ground: rural ☐
urban ☐
horizontal ☐
vertical ☐
intermediate ☐
Sand dune: stabilised tussocks ☐
blow-out ☐
dune slack ☐
Marginal: hedgerow ☐
road-side verge ☐
embankment/cutting ☐
wall ☐
earth bank ☐
Human habitation: inhabited, above ground ☐
outbuilding, above ground ☐
cellar ☐
greenhouse, unheated ☐
greenhouse, heated ☐
Aquatic: spring/small stream (< 2ft.) ☐
ditch/slow stream (2 - 10ft.) ☐
fast stream (2 - 10ft.) ☐
canal/slow river (> 10ft.) ☐
fast river (> 10ft.) ☐
puddle/tree-hole ☐
small pond/rock pool (up to c.20 sq.yd.) ☐
large pond (< 1 acre) ☐
lake (> 1 acre) ☐
sea ☐
Intertidal: very exposed ☐
exposed ☐
sheltered ☐
estuarine ☐
Cave: threshold ☐
please specify light intensity:
dark zone ☐
draft (air) ☐
no draft ☐
Soil or rock: calcareous ☐
non-calcareous ☐
pH: acidic ☐
neutral ☐
basic ☐

Figure 1b Original recording card (1968)—reverse of card

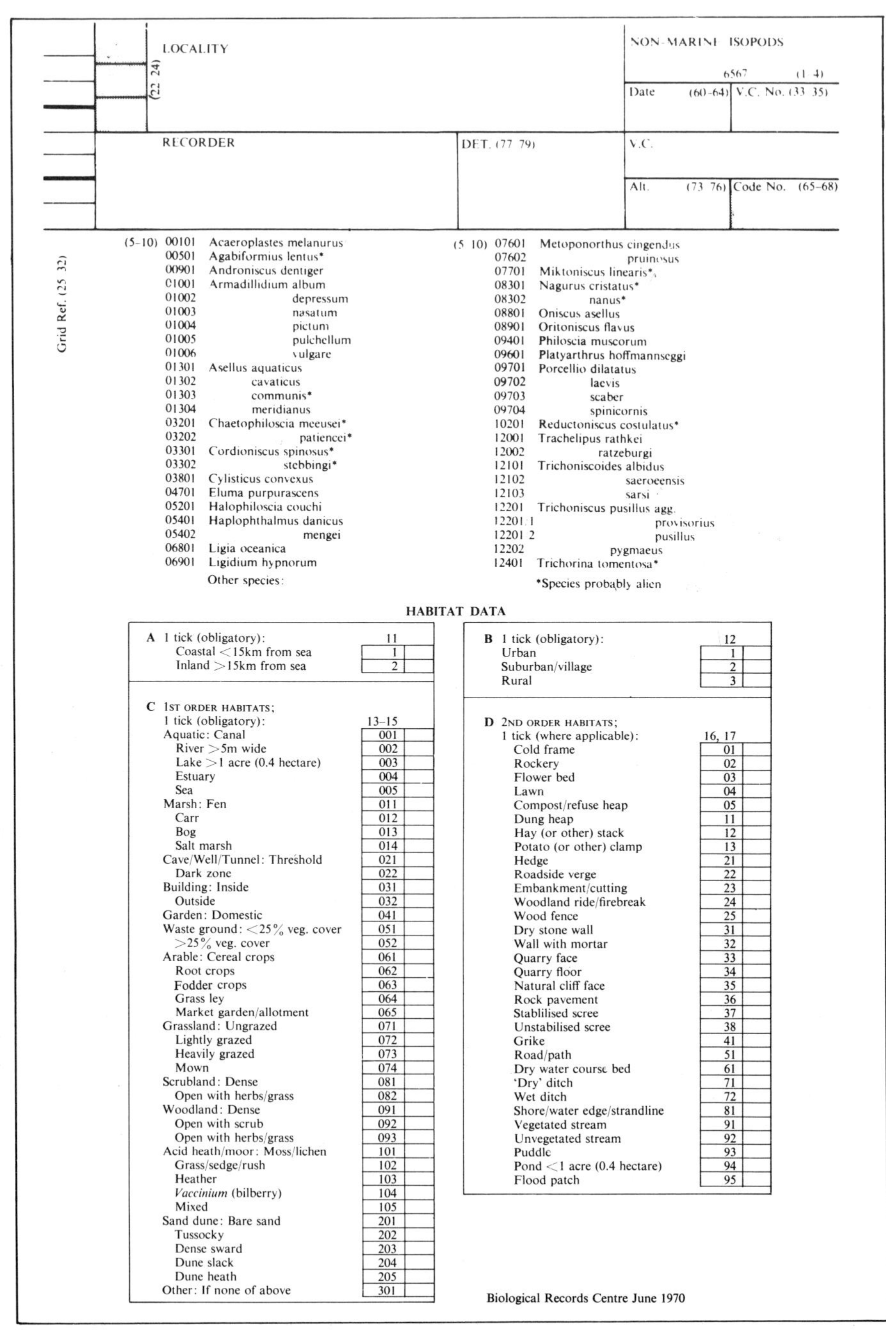

LOCALITY (22 24)

NON-MARINE ISOPODS

6567 (1 4)

Date (60-64) | V.C. No. (33 35)

RECORDER | DET. (77 79) | V.C.

Alt. (73 76) | Code No. (65-68)

Grid Ref. (25 32)

(5-10)
00101 Acaeroplastes melanurus
00501 Agabiformius lentus*
00901 Androniscus dentiger
01001 Armadillidium album
01002 depressum
01003 nasatum
01004 pictum
01005 pulchellum
01006 vulgare
01301 Asellus aquaticus
01302 cavaticus
01303 communis*
01304 meridianus
03201 Chaetophiloscia meeusei*
03202 patiencei*
03301 Cordioniscus spinosus*
03302 stebbingi*
03801 Cylisticus convexus
04701 Eluma purpurascens
05201 Halophiloscia couchi
05401 Haplophthalmus danicus
05402 mengei
06801 Ligia oceanica
06901 Ligidium hypnorum
Other species:

(5 10)
07601 Metoponorthus cingendus
07602 pruinosus
07701 Miktoniscus linearis*
08301 Nagurus cristatus*
08302 nanus*
08801 Oniscus asellus
08901 Oritoniscus flavus
09401 Philoscia muscorum
09601 Platyarthrus hoffmannseggi
09701 Porcellio dilatatus
09702 laevis
09703 scaber
09704 spinicornis
10201 Reductoniscus costulatus*
12001 Trachelipus rathkei
12002 ratzeburgi
12101 Trichoniscoides albidus
12102 saeroeensis
12103 sarsi
12201 Trichoniscus pusillus agg.
12201 1 provisorius
12201 2 pusillus
12202 pygmaeus
12401 Trichorina tomentosa*
*Species probably alien

HABITAT DATA

A 1 tick (obligatory): 11
Coastal <15km from sea | 1
Inland >15km from sea | 2

B 1 tick (obligatory): 12
Urban | 1
Suburban/village | 2
Rural | 3

C 1ST ORDER HABITATS;
1 tick (obligatory): 13–15

Habitat	Code
Aquatic: Canal	001
River >5m wide	002
Lake >1 acre (0.4 hectare)	003
Estuary	004
Sea	005
Marsh: Fen	011
Carr	012
Bog	013
Salt marsh	014
Cave/Well/Tunnel: Threshold	021
Dark zone	022
Building: Inside	031
Outside	032
Garden: Domestic	041
Waste ground: <25% veg. cover	051
>25% veg. cover	052
Arable: Cereal crops	061
Root crops	062
Fodder crops	063
Grass ley	064
Market garden/allotment	065
Grassland: Ungrazed	071
Lightly grazed	072
Heavily grazed	073
Mown	074
Scrubland: Dense	081
Open with herbs/grass	082
Woodland: Dense	091
Open with scrub	092
Open with herbs/grass	093
Acid heath/moor: Moss/lichen	101
Grass/sedge/rush	102
Heather	103
Vaccinium (bilberry)	104
Mixed	105
Sand dune: Bare sand	201
Tussocky	202
Dense sward	203
Dune slack	204
Dune heath	205
Other: If none of above	301

D 2ND ORDER HABITATS;
1 tick (where applicable): 16, 17

Habitat	Code
Cold frame	01
Rockery	02
Flower bed	03
Lawn	04
Compost/refuse heap	05
Dung heap	11
Hay (or other) stack	12
Potato (or other) clamp	13
Hedge	21
Roadside verge	22
Embankment/cutting	23
Woodland ride/firebreak	24
Wood fence	25
Dry stone wall	31
Wall with mortar	32
Quarry face	33
Quarry floor	34
Natural cliff face	35
Rock pavement	36
Stablilised scree	37
Unstabilised scree	38
Grike	41
Road/path	51
Dry water course bed	61
'Dry' ditch	71
Wet ditch	72
Shore/water edge/strandline	81
Vegetated stream	91
Unvegetated stream	92
Puddle	93
Pond <1 acre (0.4 hectare)	94
Flood patch	95

Biological Records Centre June 1970

Figure 2a Recording card in use from 1970 to 1982—front of card

HABITAT DATA

E MICROSITE (animal actually found under, on or in); 1 tick (obligatory): 36, 37

Item	Code	
Stones	01	
Shingle	02	
Soil/sand	03	
Litter	11	
Tussocks	21	
Bark (living trees or shrubs)	31	
Dead wood	32	
Dung	33	
Carrion	34	
Bracket fungi	35	
Ant colony (specify if possible)	41	
Bird/mammal nest (specify below)	51	
Rock	61	
Stone or brick work	62	
Shore line jetsam	71	
Human rubbish/garbage	81	
Other (specify below if possible)	91	

F HABITAT QUALIFIERS; 1 tick in each section, where applicable:

	38	
(a) Building: Cellar	1	
Inhabited/public	2	
Uninhabited/outbuilding	3	
Ruin	4	
Greenhouse (heated)	5	
Greenhouse (unheated)	6	

	39	
(b) Shore: Intertidal	1	
Splash zone	2	
Between splash zone and 100m	3	
100–1000m above H.W.M.	4	

	40	
(c) Encrustations: Moss	1	
Lichen	2	
Pleurococcoids	3	

	41	
(d) Waterspeed: Fast	1	
Slow	2	
Standing	3	

	42	
(e) Watercourse bed: Rocks	1	
Pebbles	2	
Sand	3	
Silt	4	
Peat	5	

G LIGHT LEVEL; 1 tick (obligatory):

	43	
Full daylight	1	
Half-light/dusk/dawn	2	
Dark	3	

Other information e.g.
Abundance,..................(number)
collected per..................(please state unit of time/space/volume) (53) Aspect/degree of slope (54)
Behaviour (55) Food (56) Predators and Parasites (57)
Age structure and Sex ratio (58) etc. (59)

H SOIL/LITTER DETAILS, terrestrial habitats only; 1 tick in each section where applicable: 44, 45

Item	Code	
(a) Litter mainly: Oak	01	
Beech	02	
Birch	03	
Sycamore	04	
Mixed deciduous	05	
Coniferous	11	
Mixed decid./conif.	21	
Gorse	31	
Hawthorn	32	
Heathers	33	
Sea Buckthorn	34	
Litter/veg. mainly: *Carex*	41	
Molinia	42	
Dactylis	43	
Festuca	44	
Bromus	45	
Brachypodium	46	
Grass—species unknown	47	
Mixed grass/herbs	51	
Nettles	61	
Reeds (*Phragmites*)	62	
Juncus	63	
Bracken	64	
Other (specify below)	71	

	46	
(b) Litter age: Fresh	1	
Old	2	
Both	3	

	47	
(c) Litter cover: Exposed	1	
Protected by thin veg.	2	
Protected by thick veg.	3	

	48	
(d) Soil/exposed rock: Calcareous	1	
Non-calcareous	2	

	49	
(e) Soil: Heavy clay	1	
Clayey	2	
Peat	3	
Loam	4	
Sandy	5	
Pure sand	6	

	50	
(f) Humus type: *Mull*	1	
Mor	2	

I LOCATION OF ANIMAL; 1 tick in each section where applicable:

	51	
(a) Horizon: >3m above ground	1	
<3m above ground	2	
On ground surface	3	
In litter	4	
<10cm in soil	5	
>10cm in soil	6	

	52	
(b) Position: In open	1	
In crevice	2	

Figure 2b Recording card in use from 1970 to 1982—reverse of card

data collected by the survey have not only allowed the original objectives of the Isopod Survey Scheme to be realized in this volume, but also provide extensive opportunities for further computer analyses which must wait until the manpower is available.

B. Data collection and validation

Considerable doubt was felt, by the organizers of the survey, about the reliability of some published records, in particular those attributable to W E Collinge (see Harding 1977). It was decided at an early stage that the survey should concentrate on collecting records from the present day, rather than abstracting published records, which were possibly unreliable. Some important museum collections (British Museum (Natural History), National Museum of Ireland, Yorkshire Museum) have been examined and resultant checked identifications of uncommon species used to augment the recent records from the survey. Several private collections have also been examined. Comprehensive bibliographies of publications relating to the occurrence of woodlice in the British Isles have been published (Harding 1977; Doogue & Harding 1982), or are in preparation (Harding, in preparation).

Recorders were issued with recording cards and a set of *Instructions to collectors* (see Appendix 4). This 4-page card was the chief means of establishing a standard, reliable, procedure for the assessment of the woodlouse diversity, in any particular area. The aim was to produce a small group of thorough and prolific collectors, producing accurate and unbiased records. (The question of bias in recording is discussed below.) The card gave directions as to the best methods of collecting different kinds of woodlice (at least as known to the organizers of the survey in June 1970). It also gave detailed guidance on the completion of the recording card, with sections on the correct way to give a grid reference and emphasis on the fact that a new card was needed for each locality, each microsite and each date of collecting. (The term 'microsite' was preferred to 'microhabitat' because it referred only to where an animal was actually found, with no implication that it normally lived there.) Recorders were encouraged to give as much detail as possible by filling in Sections F to I of the recording card.

The *Instructions* card was supplemented by articles in the Isopod Survey Scheme newsletter on particular collecting techniques, habitats and problems of identification. Difficulties were experienced in filling out the recording card. The mildly interested were frightened off altogether, which at least had the merit of allowing the organizers time to correspond with the serious recorders at some length. For those who persevered, the chief problems were (i) the cut-and-dried nature of categories on the card, which often seemed to need qualifying (this was not acceptable as the card was designed to provide computer input), (ii) the need to tick more than one category in some sections (again this was not acceptable), and (iii) the difficulty of establishing an agreed meaning for such terms as *Fresh litter* and *Humus type: Mull.*

To a considerable extent, these problems were resolved during the later stages of the survey by field meetings, during which common interpretations of card categories could be established, but readers of the species accounts should note that not every category meant precisely the same thing to all recorders at every stage of the survey.

The greatest problem facing collectors was, however, bias in recording in favour of large, surface-living species.

Trichoniscus pygmaeus, Haplophthalmus mengei and other soil-living species require a specialist approach for successful detection, and were seldom found by some recorders. Sieving techniques developed by conchologists proved one of the most effective ways of finding the tiny species in the field, but were not used before 1975. These specialist techniques were used in Ireland and Scotland, but the major use was concentrated in the south-east of Britain, so there is a possible regional bias, with true diversity in the north and west under-estimated. However, specialist techniques have contributed to less than 5% of total records, so that this effect must be small. The consensus among experienced recorders is that there is certainly some bias towards the larger species in the records made, and that special attention needs to be paid to the distribution of trichoniscids in the north.

Other forms of bias encountered include seasonal variation in the activity of recorders, and in the holiday locations and domicile of the most active recorders. Very few records (less than 3%) have been made at night, with consequent under-recording of crevice-living species, such as *Ligia oceanica*, as well as more subtle distortions of reality. For example, day-time recording of *Porcellio spinicornis* can result in a bias towards dry stone walls, where it is easily found by lifting the top stones. On the walls of buildings, it is difficult to locate by day, as it shelters in crevices, but it is obvious at night when it comes out to feed on lichens and algae on the surface.

These forms of bias have been countered by deliberate efforts to visit under-recorded areas, and to collect at all seasons and at all times of the day and night. The Irish recorders have been outstandingly successful in achieving balanced coverage, even in the troubled areas of the Northern Ireland border. Individual species accounts note any bias to which records of species are particularly prone.

Records were validated by G M and V D Collis, D Doogue, P T Harding, P G Oliver and S L Sutton, with confirmation from others as necessary. Details on the completed cards sent in were checked, especially grid references. Records outside the known range of a species were double-checked, as were those referring to unusual habitats. Voucher specimens were required for all species from new recorders. These specimens were returned so that each recorder could build up a reference collection. Any species new to a recorder had to be supported by specimens. In the process, central reference collections were built up at Monks Wood, Leeds University and the National Museum of Wales.

'Critical' species, where mis-identification was likely, were the subject of particular attention. In general, the organizers feel that validation procedures were thorough and effective in preventing errors in identity.

The following species were found to cause problems:

Ligidium hypnorum	easily mistaken for	*Philoscia muscorum*
Haplophthalmus danicus		*H. mengei*
Trichoniscoides albidus		*Trichoniscus pusillus*
Trichoniscoides sarsi		*T. saeroeensis*
Trichoniscus pygmaeus		*T. pusillus* juveniles
Armadillidium album		*A. vulgare* juveniles
Armadillidium pictum		*A. pulchellum*
Armadillidium pulchellum		*A. vulgare* juveniles
Porcellio dilatatus		*P. scaber*
Porcellionides cingendus		*Philoscia muscorum*

C. Data storage and data processing

The original record cards submitted by recorders were retained by the survey organizer. All these cards have now been deposited at BRC to form part of its archive supporting the computerized data-bank. Copies of the record cards from Ireland have been deposited at the Irish Biological Records Centre in Dublin.

Since 1975, computer punched cards have been prepared from the data on the original record cards. It had always been intended that the computer analysis of habitat data on woodlice would be made in conjunction with similar analyses of data on myriapods. In 1975, C P Fairhurst began to develop the analysis of habitat data on woodlice and myriapods on the ICL 1904S computer at Salford University, using a standard SPSS package (Statistical Package for Social Scientists) (Fairhurst, Barber & Armitage 1978). Several preliminary analyses of data on woodlice were made and detailed analyses of 16000 records were made by Fairhurst in 1979.

In 1981, improved computer facilities at BRC, and assistance with data preparation and programming from the NERC Computing Services staff at

Monks Wood, enabled the woodlice data to be mounted on the DEC PDP 11/34 mini-computer at Monks Wood.

Validated listings of records were produced in 1981, and interim distribution maps and analyses of habitat data were prepared in the spring of 1982. All the records received by the survey, up to the end of August 1982, were on computer file by the end of that year. The completed data set comprised 27 128 records, of which 23 499 included some habitat data (Table 1). From this data-set, the final distribution maps were run in January 1983, using the FR80 high-precision film-recorder at the SERC Rutherford/Appleton Laboratories (RAL), accessed by a dedicated line from the PDP mini-computer at

Table 1 Summary, by species, of the complete data set

	Number and percentage of all records		Number and percentage of records with habitat data	
Acaeroplastes melanurus	1	(<0.01%)	—	—
Androniscus dentiger	738	(2.72%)	608	(2.59%)
Armadillidium album	45	(0.16%)	44	(0.19%)
A. depressum	121	(0.45%)	100	(0.43%)
A. nasatum	158	(0.58%)	113	(0.48%)
A. pictum	8	(0.03%)	7	(0.03%)
A. pulchellum	98	(0.36%)	72	(0.31%)
A. vulgare	2116	(7.80%)	1813	(7.72%)
Buddelundiella cataractae	5	(0.02%)	5	(0.02%)
Cylisticus convexus	158	(0.58%)	119	(0.51%)
Eluma purpurascens	37	(0.14%)	36	(0.15%)
Halophiloscia couchi	42	(0.15%)	35	(0.15%)
Haplophthalmus danicus	190	(0.70%)	146	(0.62%)
H. mengei	290	(1.07%)	260	(1.11%)
Ligia oceanica	863	(3.18%)	700	(2.98%)
Ligidium hypnorum	131	(0.48%)	102	(0.43%)
Metatrichoniscoides celticus	8	(0.03%)	8	(0.03%)
Miktoniscus patiencei	22	(0.08%)	16	(0.07%)
Oniscus asellus	6501	(23.96%)	5624	(23.93%)
Oritoniscus flavus	55	(0.20%)	44	(0.19%)
Philoscia muscorum	3773	(13.91%)	3343	(14.23%)
Platyarthrus hoffmannseggi	542	(1.99%)	452	(1.92%)
Porcellio dilatatus	72	(0.26%)	39	(0.17%)
P. laevis	41	(0.15%)	24	(0.10%)
P. scaber	5361	(19.76%)	4678	(19.91%)
P. spinicornis	398	(1.47%)	362	(1.54%)
Porcellionides cingendus	376	(1.39%)	321	(1.37%)
P. pruinosus	214	(0.79%)	165	(0.70%)
Stenophiloscia zosterae	5	(0.02%)	5	(0.02%)
Trachelipus rathkei	84	(0.31%)	70	(0.30%)
Trichoniscoides albidus	50	(0.18%)	22	(0.09%)
T. saeroeensis	74	(0.27%)	65	(0.28%)
T. sarsi	15	(0.05%)	11	(0.05%)
Trichoniscus pusillus	3974	(14.65%)	3573	(15.20%)
T. pygmaeus	557	(2.05%)	484	(2.06%)
Total number of records	27 128		23 499	

Monks Wood. This is the standard procedure for map production by BRC because its data-bank is held on the IBM computer system at RAL, using the G-EXEC management system. The analyses of the habitat data were made in January 1983 to give listings, for each species, of the number and percentage of records in each habitat feature. Subsequent analyses were made of the data to provide, for each habitat feature, the percentage of records of each species.

IV DISTRIBUTION MAPS AND SPECIES ACCOUNTS

The following Section provides distribution maps and accounts of all native and naturalized species recorded from the British Isles, except *Acaeroplastes melanurus* which is believed to be extinct (see page 17). Alien species are not included (see page 17).

Distribution maps for species

The distribution map of each species shows the recorded occurrence in the British Isles, using the 10 km squares of the British and Irish National Grids as mapping units (and for the Channel Isles the Universal Transverse Mercator Grid). Distribution records have been differentiated to show those 10 km squares for which there is only a record from before 1970 (○) and those for which there is at least one record in the period 1970-82 inclusive (●).

Distribution map—all records

The facing map shows the coverage of records mapped using 10 km grid squares as described above, but using 3 symbols to differentiate the total number of species recorded in each square: • 1–5 species, ● 6–10 species, ⬤ 11 or more species. Blank squares, of which there are 737, indicate that there are no records of woodlice, due, in all probability, to an absence of recording rather than an absence of woodlice. The total number of 10 km squares with some land in the British Isles (including the Channel Isles) is 3 870. The survey received records for 3 133 squares (80.95% of the total), 2 188 in Britain, 9 in the Channel Isles and 936 in Ireland. All coastal squares have been included; in some cases, small offshore islands (eg Grassholm, Skellig Michael) appear as records in the sea because the digitized base map is too small to show these small islands.

Species accounts

Each account begins with a simple description of the species, incorporating field characters which aid identification of live specimens. These descriptions are not intended to replace the existing keys (Edney 1954; Sutton 1972, 1980) for identification. Notes on the history of their occurrence are included for some uncommon, or recently discovered, species.

The *Habitat data* section analyses the data recorded during the survey following the sections (C = 1st Order Habitat, E = Microsite, etc), and features within these sections, of the recording card (Figure 2). For each habitat feature, the number of records of the particular species is expressed as a percentage of the total number of records of the species with habitat data in that section. Thus, for *Ligia oceanica* (page 34):

Habitat data

A	(700)	Coastal 100%
(1) Section A of recording card	(2) Number of records of *L. oceanica* with data in Section A	(3) All 700 records with data in Section A were recorded as *Coastal*

Some features within Sections C and D have been amalgamated to consolidate information and help interpretation (eg in Section C, all *Woodland* can be expressed as a single percentage). Habitat features and sub-sections with less than 5% of the records of the relevant species have been omitted, and some consistently poorly recorded sub-sections (eg F(c) *Encrustations*, H(c) *Litter cover* and H(f) *Humus type*) have not been included in the summary of the analyses. Particular bias to records from 'synanthropic' habitat features in Sections C and D has been noted for some species.

Subsequent paragraphs comment on both the habitat data and distribution maps, providing additional information on the occurrence and behaviour of the species. Reference is also made to any research done recently on the species in the British Isles. Brief statements on the occurrence of each species outside the British Isles have been drawn mainly from Vandel (1960a, 1962).

Localities mentioned in the text are drawn from the place-names given on record cards and, for earlier records, from museum data labels and publications. Almost all the sites mentioned are on privately owned land or on nature reserves, and therefore may not be accessible to the general public. We have decided to cite counties as the Watson/Praeger biological vice-counties (see Figure 3 and Table 2; Dandy 1969; Scannell & Synnott 1972; Webb 1980) because of the instability of administrative county boundaries in Britain.

The scientific names and English names of vascular plants follow Clapham, Tutin and Warburg (1981). The scientific names of ants follow Bolton and Collingwood (1975).

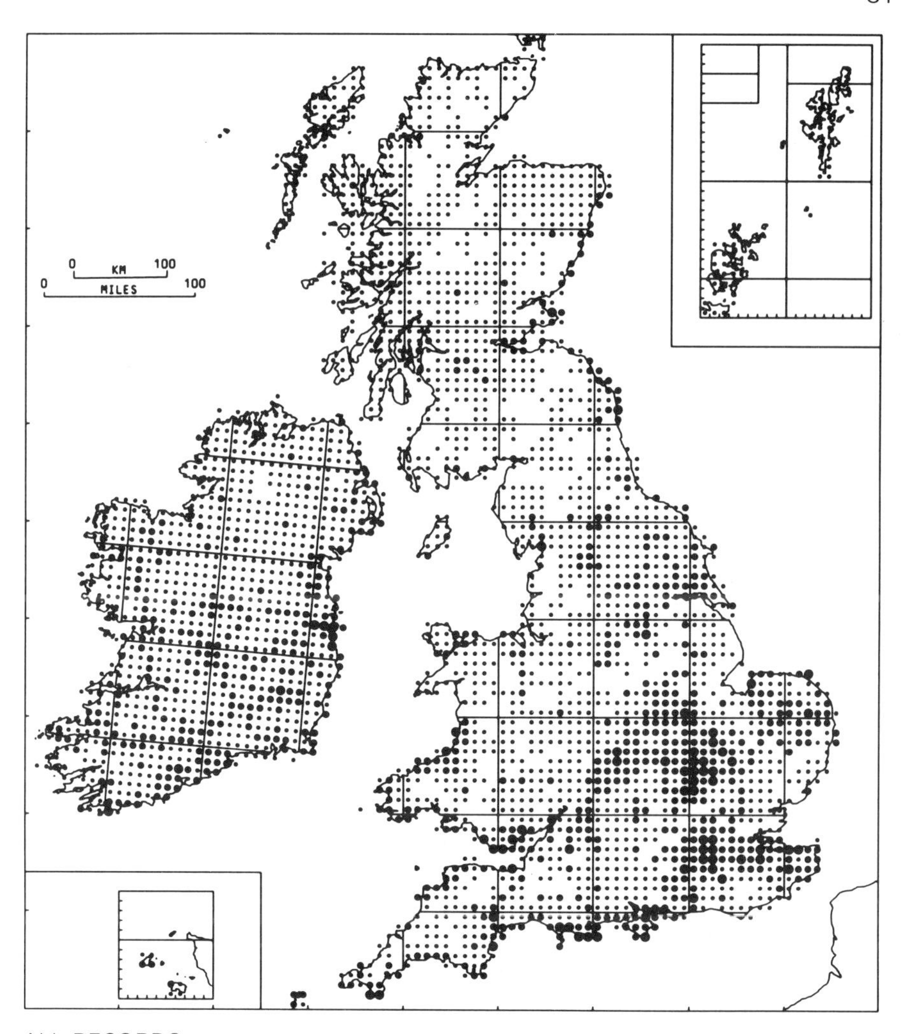

ALL RECORDS

Number of records received: 27 128

England:	14 768 records	(54%)	Channel Islands:	92 records	(<1%)
Wales:	1 965 records	(7%)	Ireland:	5 963 records	(22%)
Scotland:	4 256 records	(16%)	Eire:	5 242 records	(19%)
Isle of Man:	84 records	(<1%)	Northern Ireland:	721 records	(3%)

Number of 10 km squares in which recorded: 3 133
Number (%) of records with some habitat data: 23 499 (86%)
Number (%) of records from 1970 onwards: 24 712 (91%)

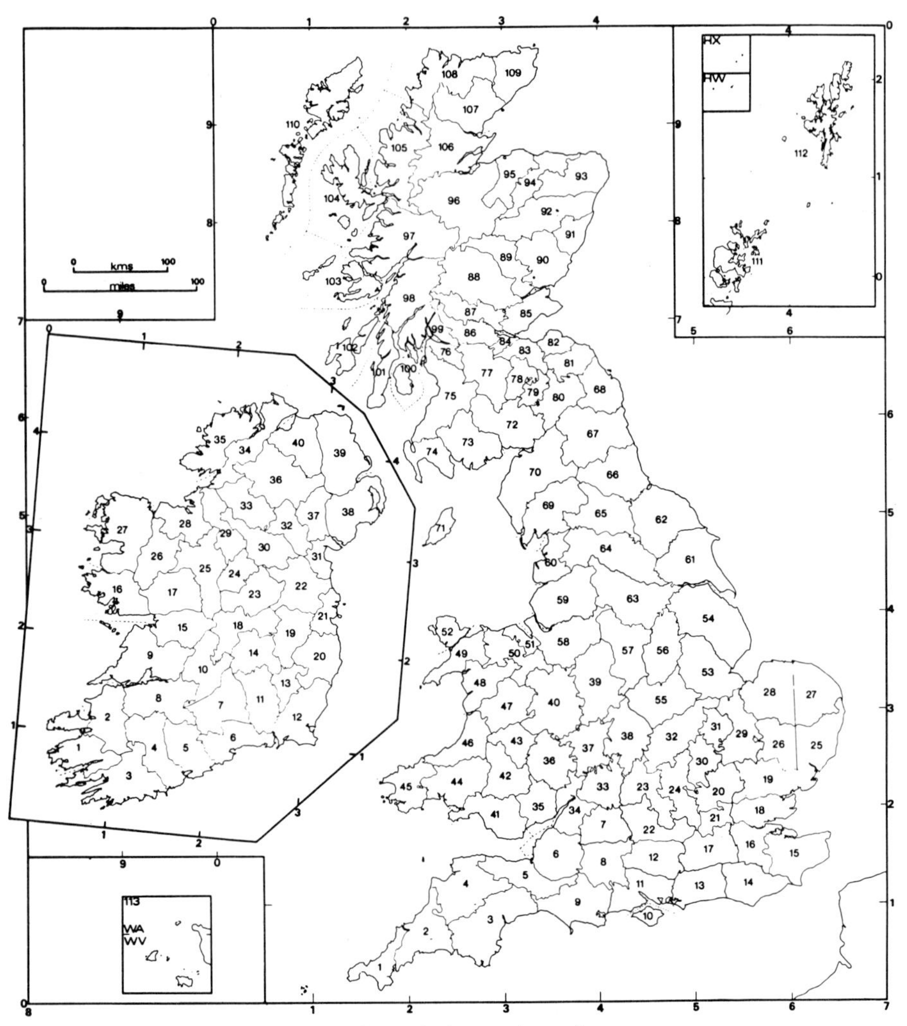

Figure 3 Biological vice-county boundaries and numbers

Table 2 Biological vice-counties, numbers and names

England and Wales

1. West Cornwall (with Scilly)
2. East Cornwall
3. South Devon
4. North Devon
5. South Somerset
6. North Somerset
7. North Wiltshire
8. South Wiltshire
9. Dorset
10. Isle of Wight
11. South Hampshire
12. North Hampshire
13. West Sussex
14. East Sussex
15. East Kent
16. West Kent
17. Surrey
18. South Essex
19. North Essex
20. Hertfordshire
21. Middlesex
22. Berkshire
23. Oxfordshire
24. Buckinghamshire
25. East Suffolk
26. West Suffolk
27. East Norfolk
28. West Norfolk
29. Cambridgeshire
30. Bedfordshire
31. Huntingdonshire
32. Northamptonshire
33. East Gloucestershire
34. West Gloucestershire
35. Monmouthshire
36. Herefordshire
37. Worcestershire
38. Warwickshire
39. Staffordshire
40. Shropshire (Salop)
41. Glamorgan
42. Breconshire
43. Radnorshire
44. Carmarthenshire
45. Pembrokeshire
46. Cardiganshire
47. Montgomeryshire
48. Merionethshire
49. Caernarvonshire
50. Denbighshire
51. Flintshire
52. Anglesey
53. South Lincolnshire
54. North Lincolnshire
55. Leicestershire (with Rutland)
56. Nottinghamshire
57. Derbyshire
58. Cheshire
59. South Lancashire
60. West Lancashire
61. South-east Yorkshire
62. North-east Yorkshire
63. South-west Yorkshire
64. Mid-west Yorkshire
65. North-west Yorkshire
66. Durham
67. South Northumberland
68. North Northumberland (Cheviot)
69. Westmorland with North Lancashire
70. Cumberland
71. Isle of Man
113. Channel Isles

Scotland

72. Dumfries-shire
73. Kirkcudbrightshire
74. Wigtownshire
75. Ayrshire
76. Renfrewshire
77. Lanarkshire
78. Peebles-shire
79. Selkirkshire
80. Roxburghshire
81. Berwickshire
82. East Lothian (Haddington)
83. Midlothian (Edinburgh)
84. West Lothian (Linlithgow)
85. Fifeshire (with Kinross)
86. Stirlingshire
87. West Perthshire (with Clackmannan)
88. Mid Perthshire
89. East Perthshire
90. Angus (Forfar)
91. Kincardineshire
92. South Aberdeenshire
93. North Aberdeenshire
94. Banffshire
95. Moray (Elgin)
96. East Inverness-shire (with Nairn)
97. West Inverness-shire
98. Argyll Main
99. Dunbartonshire
100. Clyde Isles
101. Kintyre
102. South Ebudes
103. Mid Ebudes
104. North Ebudes
105. Wester Ross
106. Easter Ross
107. East Sutherland
108. West Sutherland
109. Caithness
110. Outer Hebrides
111. Orkney Islands
112. Shetland Islands (Zetland)

Ireland

H.1. South Kerry
H.2. North Kerry
H.3. West Cork
H.4. Mid Cork
H.5. East Cork
H.6. Waterford
H.7. South Tipperary
H.8. Limerick
H.9. Clare
H.10. North Tipperary
H.11. Kilkenny
H.12. Wexford
H.13. Carlow
H.14. Laois (Queen's County)
H.15. South-east Galway
H.16. West Galway
H.17. North-east Galway
H.18. Offaly (King's County)
H.19. Kildare
H.20. Wicklow
H.21. Dublin
H.22. Meath
H.23. Westmeath
H.24. Longford
H.25. Roscommon
H.26. East Mayo
H.27. West Mayo
H.28. Sligo
H.29. Leitrim
H.30. Cavan
H.31. Louth
H.32. Monaghan
H.33. Fermanagh
H.34. East Donegal
H.35. West Donegal
H.36. Tyrone
H.37. Armagh
H.38. Down
H.39. Antrim
H.40. Londonderry

LIGIA OCEANICA (Linnaeus)

Ligia oceanica is the largest species of British woodlouse, with some specimens exceeding 30 mm in length. The colour varies from a mottled dark grey-green to a uniform light grey-brown, depending on the dilation of closely packed chromatophores below the cuticle. Two light-coloured patches occur either side of the median line of the dorsal surface. Large black eyes, long antennae, characteristic uropods, large size and habitat make this a distinctive species. The only possible confusion is likely to be with *Halophiloscia couchi.*

Habitat data

A (700 records): Coastal 100%.
B (696 records): Rural 83%, Suburban/village 13%, Urban 4%.
C (700 records): Sea 77%, Estuary 9%, Salt marsh 6%.
D (631 records): Shore, etc, 84%, Natural cliff face 8%, Wall with mortar 3%.
E (692 records): Stones 56%, Rock 16%, Shingle 12%, Shoreline jetsam 6%, Stone or brickwork 5%.
F (b) Shore (600 records): Intertidal 47%, Splash zone 46%, Between splash zone and 100 m 7%.
H (d) Soil/exposed rock (263 records): Non-calcareous 78%, Calcareous 22%.

L. oceanica is nocturnal and can be difficult to find in daylight at sites where it may be abundant at night. Despite this difficulty, from a total of 695 records, 91% were made in *full daylight*, 3% in *half light* and only 6% in the *dark*!

L. oceanica is common on rocky shores all round the coast. Where the coast is unsuitable, such as extensive parts of south-east England and East Anglia, it may be found on harbour and sea walls, wooden jetty piles, etc. The only habitat requirements seem to be a solid substrate, within reach of the sea, with crevices in which the animals can take refuge. *L. oceanica* can be found on both very exposed and very sheltered shores. It is able to withstand reduced salinities (Parry 1953) and has been recorded in river estuaries where there is suitable rocky habitat (Percival 1929).

In winter, *L. oceanica* may migrate up the shore in exposed situations (eg O'Connor 1945), and can be found under stones in rock-pools where these occur high up on the shore. It is occasionally recorded with other species, particularly *Porcellio scaber* and *H. couchi.*

Further afield, *L. oceanica* has been recorded all along the Atlantic coast of western Europe from Norway and as far south as Morocco, according to Vandel (1960a). It is absent from the Eastern Baltic, but occurs on the Faroe Islands and the southern shores of Iceland. It seems to have been first recorded in the USA from Rhode Island in 1880 (Swan 1956); new records of populations of this species on the New England coast continue to be published (Dexter 1959, 1972), and may indicate that this species is spreading following introduction by man.

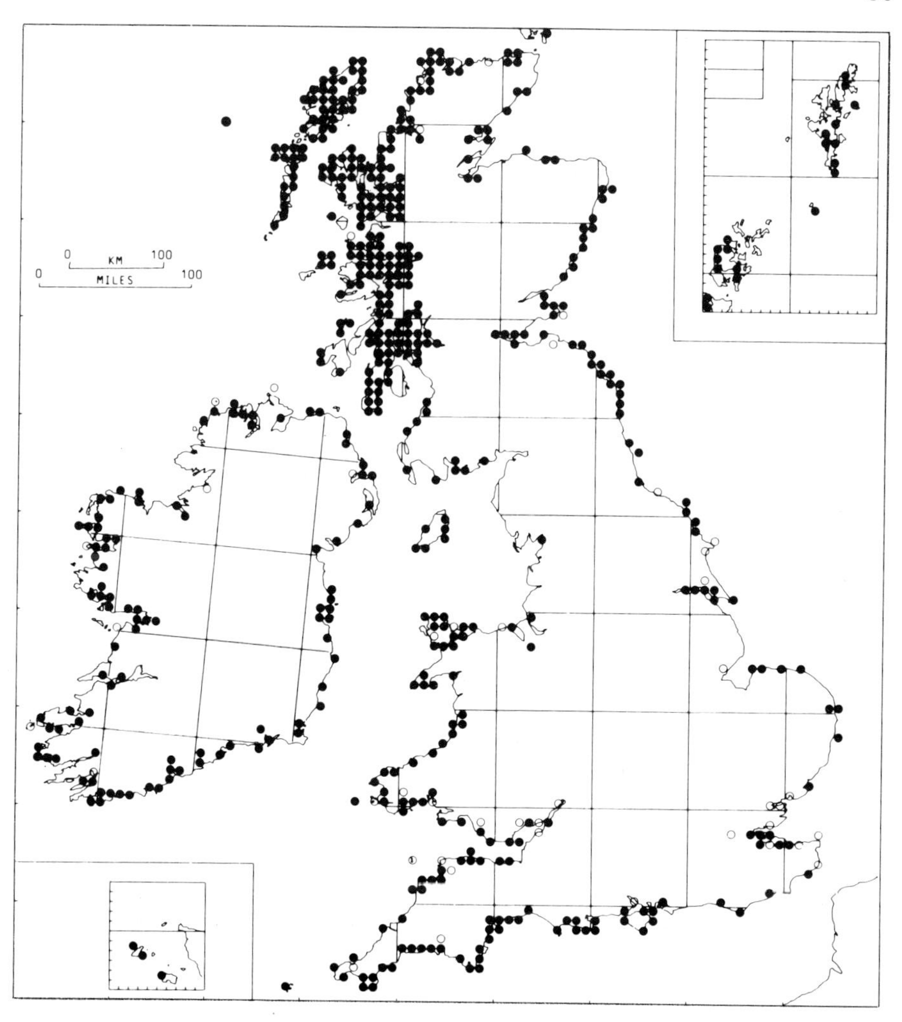

LIGIA OCEANICA

Number of records received: 863

England:	238 records	(28%)	Channel Islands:	3 records	(<1%)
Wales:	86 records	(10%)	Ireland:	121 records	(14%)
Scotland:	394 records	(46%)	Eire:	100 records	(12%)
Isle of Man:	21 records	(2%)	Northern Ireland:	21 records	(2%)

Number of 10 km squares in which recorded:	569	
Number (%) of records with some habitat data:	700	(81%)
Number (%) of records from 1970 onwards:	745	(86%)

LIGIDIUM HYPNORUM (Cuvier)

Ligidium hypnorum is dark, shiny and active; it resembles a poorly patterned, dark specimen of *Philoscia muscorum* and is not unlike the Irish species *Oritoniscus flavus*. It moves rapidly when disturbed, soon finding shelter in the damp leaf litter and plant debris among which it is usually found. It rarely exceeds 9 mm in length.

The species was first recorded in Britain from Copthorne Common, Surrey (Stebbing 1873). The majority of subsequent records have been from south-eastern England. Several early records from the west and north of England have not been substantiated, either by voucher material or by recent records. It should be sought at these earlier sites along the banks of the River Bollin between Bowdon and Ashley Mills, Cheshire (Collinge 1917), and at Raven Meols near Formby, South Lancashire (Standen 1922).

Habitat data

A (102 records): Inland 85%, Coastal 15%.
B (102 records): Rural 92%, Suburban/village 8%
C (102 records): Woodland 45%, Fen 18%, Grassland, ungrazed and lightly grazed 12%, Carr 10%, Waste ground 6%.
D (47 records): Water edge 28%, Ditches 19%, Roadside verge & Embankment/cutting 17%, Dry watercourse bed 11%, Flood patch 9%.
E (101 records): Litter 43%, Dead wood 27%, Tussocks 13%, Stones 10%.
H (a) Litter type (66 records): Mixed deciduous 20%, Oak and beech 15%, Reeds *(Phragmites)* 15%, Mixed grass/herbs 14%.
H (e) Soil (57 records): Peat 35%, Clayey 26%, Loam 25%.

The data available on habitats show that *L. hypnorum* occurs mainly in deciduous woodlands and in fen areas. This analysis accords well with the habitats described by continental authors (Meinertz 1950; Vandel 1960a). Many localities, particularly towards the west and north of its range, are known to be ancient woods (eg Lower Wetmoor Wood, West Gloucestershire; Wayland Wood, West Norfolk), relatively undisturbed fens (eg Woodwalton Fen, Huntingdonshire and Chippenham Fen, Cambridgeshire) or river valleys (eg Wiltshire Avon). This occurrence, together with its absence from synanthropic sites, suggests that *L. hypnorum* is a relic of the fauna of the humid, deciduous forests, with abundant wet areas and small pools, that covered southern Britain prior to the Bronze Age.

The map shows a widespread occurrence in Kent, Surrey, and parts of Sussex and Hampshire; it is, for example, abundant in the Wealden oakwoods. It also occurs sparsely in East Anglia, in woods and fens; and in West Gloucestershire and North Somerset, in woods and beside watercourses. The absence of records from the south-western peninsula appears to be real; suitable localities have been examined by several experienced recorders (eg the Somerset Levels, and woods in the Fowey valley, East Cornwall). The north-western limits of distribution are difficult to define: a record from a lake in Gumley Wood, Leicestershire, suggests that *L. hypnorum* may occur more widely in the east midlands than would seem to be the case at present.

L. hypnorum has been recorded widely across central Europe, as far east as the north-eastern shores of the Black Sea. It has not been recorded in the Mediterranean basin. In the north, its limits are in England, Denmark, the extreme south of Sweden and the Baltic coast of the USSR (Estonia).

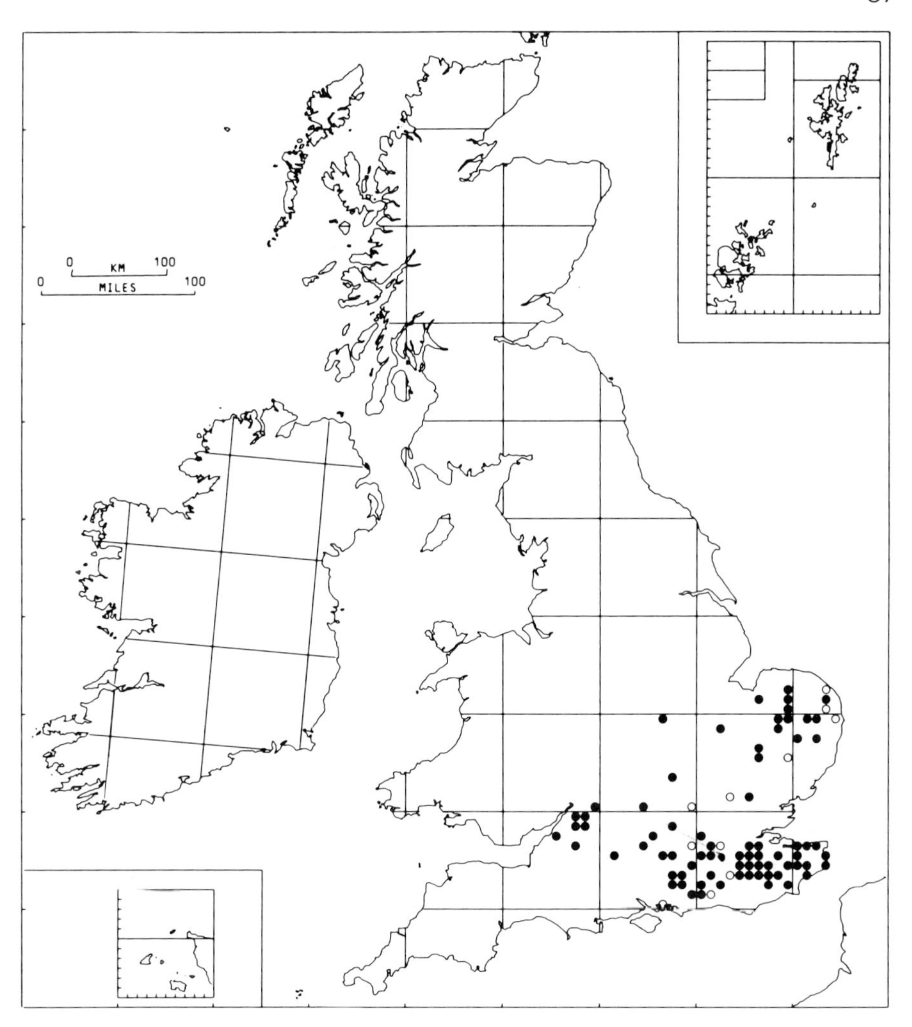

LIGIDIUM HYPNORUM

Number of records received: 131

England: 131 records (100%)

Number of 10 km squares in which recorded: 84
Number (%) of records with some habitat data: 102 (78%)
Number (%) of records from 1970 onwards: 104 (79%)

ANDRONISCUS DENTIGER Verhoeff

Androniscus dentiger is a distinctively coloured animal varying from very pale flesh-pink to, more typically, a rich rose-red. It has a broad yellow median stripe, through which the dark-coloured gut contents are visible, giving the impression that there is also a dark dorso-median stripe. The body colour fades rapidly to white in alcohol. Viewed under a hand-lens, the body is clearly tuberculate and the eyes are each of a single ocellus. Adults are 5–6 mm long, males tending to be somewhat smaller than females. It has been most frequently recorded from synanthropic sites, but caves, screes, maritime cliff faces and shorelines appear to be true natural habitats.

Habitat data

A (608 records): Inland 60%, Coastal 40%.
B (608 records): Rural 49%, Suburban/village 34%, Urban 17%.
C (608 records): Waste ground 27%, Garden 22%, Building 14%, Grassland 14%. Records from synanthropic sites (excluding Waste ground) 38%.
D (362 records): Quarry floor 10%, Roadside verge 10%, Wall with mortar 10%, Road/path 9%, Shore, etc, 9%, Rockery 7%, Embankment/cutting 6%, Natural cliff face 6%. Records from synanthropic sites 74%.
E (603 records): Stones 51%, Stone or brickwork 11%, Dead wood 8%, Human rubbish/garbage 7%, Soil/sand 5%, Litter 5%, Rock 5%.
H (d) Soil/exposed rock (249 records): Calcareous 62%, Non-calcareous 38%.

This species appears to be widespread in England, Wales and Ireland. There are comparatively few records from Scotland, where it seems to be genuinely less widespread and frequent. It is certainly under-recorded, at least in England and Wales, as the records show considerable recorder bias.

It appears to be capable of tolerating a wide range of humidity levels from, for example, relatively dry mortar and cement between the stones of old buildings, to the aqueous layer surrounding stones in wet ditches, stream-margins, and wet patches below springs. Its synanthropic associations are clear; piles of domestic rubbish and heaps of old bricks and rubble, especially those with mortar, are very reliable sites for finding this species. It has been widely recorded in association with churches in southern Ireland, Wales and parts of England. Natural sites where it has been recorded include caves, potholes, cliff faces and shorelines: it is sometimes abundant in maritime shingle, and on sea cliffs, in the splash zone, and is probably much more widespread in these sites than the records suggest. It was the most commonly recorded species in caves, mines and tunnels, but most records from such sites did not include habitat data; thus, the above analysis (section C) does not bring out the importance of subterranean sites. It is only occasionally seen in the open, apparently occupying the same microsites by night and day, except on sea cliffs where it is sometimes seen in abundance, in the open, at night.

A. dentiger has been recorded from western Europe, extending eastwards to south-west Germany and north-west Yugoslavia, southwards to North Africa and northwards to Scotland and Holland, but not from Spain and Portugal; it has been found as an introduction in glasshouses as far north as Finland, and also in Canada.

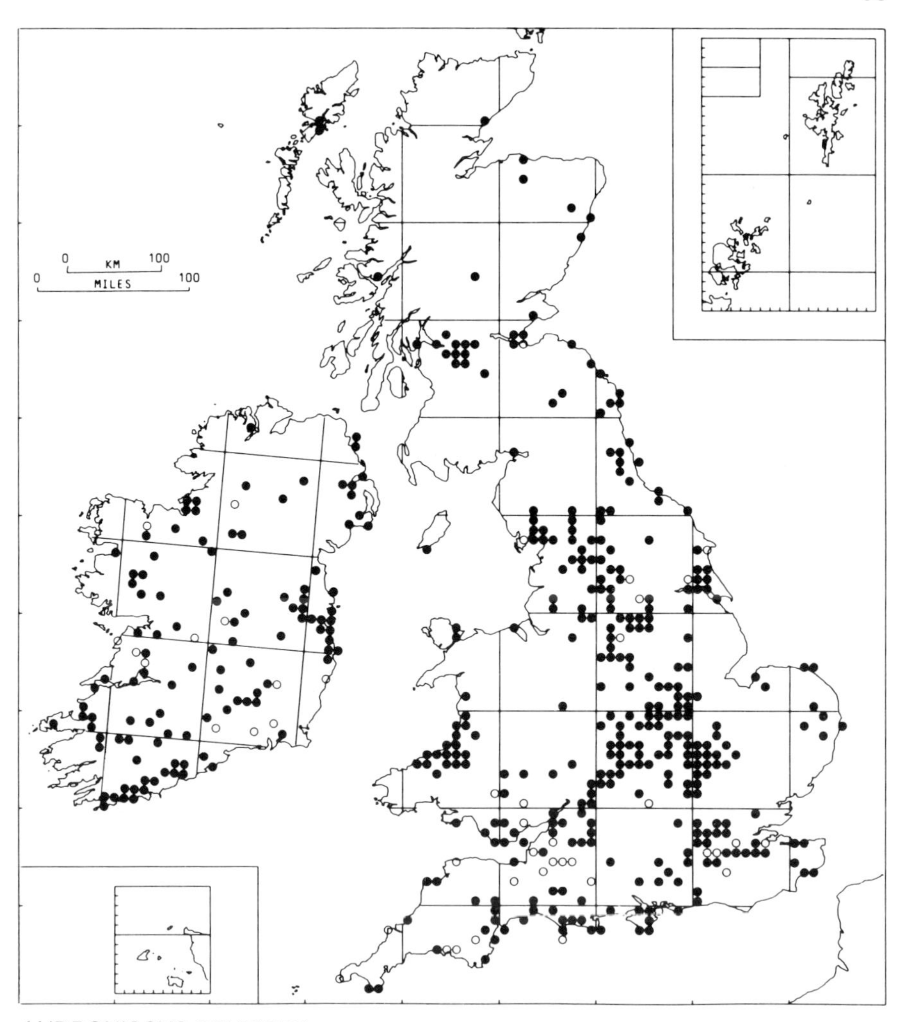

ANDRONISCUS DENTIGER

Number of records received: 738

England:	463 records	(63%)
Wales:	61 records	(8%)
Scotland:	64 records	(9%)
Isle of Man:	1 record	(<1%)
Ireland:	149 records	(20%)
Eire:	133 records	(18%)
Northern Ireland:	16 records	(2%)

Number of 10 km squares in which recorded:	472	
Number (%) of records with some habitat data:	608	(82%)
Number (%) of records from 1970 onwards:	636	(86%)

BUDDELUNDIELLA CATARACTAE Verhoeff

It is easy to overlook this tiny woodlouse, as, when rolled up, it resembles a grain of sand. The small size (to 4 mm) and inconspicuous appearance of *Buddelundiella cataractae* probably account for its late discovery in Britain, and for the paucity of records. The habit of rolling into a loose ball, and the haplophthalmoid tergal sculpture are sufficient to distinguish *B. cataractae* from all other native British woodlice (the exotic glasshouse genus *Reductoniscus* is superficially similar). In Europe, within the genus, the pleon sculpture has been used as a major diagnostic character. In *B. cataractae*, this sculpture consists of 2 pairs of low tubercles on the fourth pleonite. The colour varies from white (young specimens), through slightly pink, to buff (large specimens).

Oliver (1983) was the first to record *B. cataractae* in Britain, from specimens collected in a domestic garden in Cardiff, in 1981. The following year, it was found in a shingle bank at Snettisham, West Norfolk. This discovery led to the examination of a similar site at Barry, Glamorgan, where it was also found. (It has since been found in riverside gravels in Cardiff.)

Specimens from the garden in Cardiff have been recorded, from April to November, from under stones and loose paving. The Snettisham site, however, is a natural habitat consisting of a stable shingle bank, thinly covered with the grass *Arrhenatherum elatius. B. cataractae* was found here down to a depth of 80 cm in the shingle, but was most abundant between 10 and 20 cm. At Barry, the site is slightly above the extreme high water mark of spring tides where the strandline consists of small pebbles. At a depth of between 10-20 cm, the interstices between the pebbles are filled with a damp, humus-rich soil, in which *B. cataractae* was found. At both coastal sites, the associated isopod species included *Haplophthalmus mengei, Trichoniscus pusillus, Armadillidium vulgare* and *Androniscus dentiger. B. cataractae* was the dominant species at Snettisham, with densities of over 6000 m^2 recorded.

The wide geographic separation of the British records suggests that *B. cataractae* may be found at many suitable sites around the coast of Britain, but special collecting techniques need to be employed. Hand searching, in humus-rich soil at Barry, revealed the species, but A G Irwin (BISG newsletter no. 16, 1982) advocated gently washing shingle through sieves as the most effective method.

Abroad, this species is known from scattered localities throughout Europe: France, the eastern Mediterranean area, Finland, Hungary and Georgia SSR. Caruso and Brisolese (1974) considered that it occurs as a native species throughout south-eastern Europe, from the French Alps to Georgia, and that these occurrences (except those in glasshouses) represent a wide paleo-European origin of pre-Quaternary date. This view conflicts with Vandel's (1960a) opinion that *B. cataractae* originated only in the Yugoslavian region and has spread elsewhere by the influence of man. The few British records suggest native populations, especially at the 2 coastal sites. The distribution and habitat of this species are clearly so inadequately recorded that conclusions about either are inappropriate.

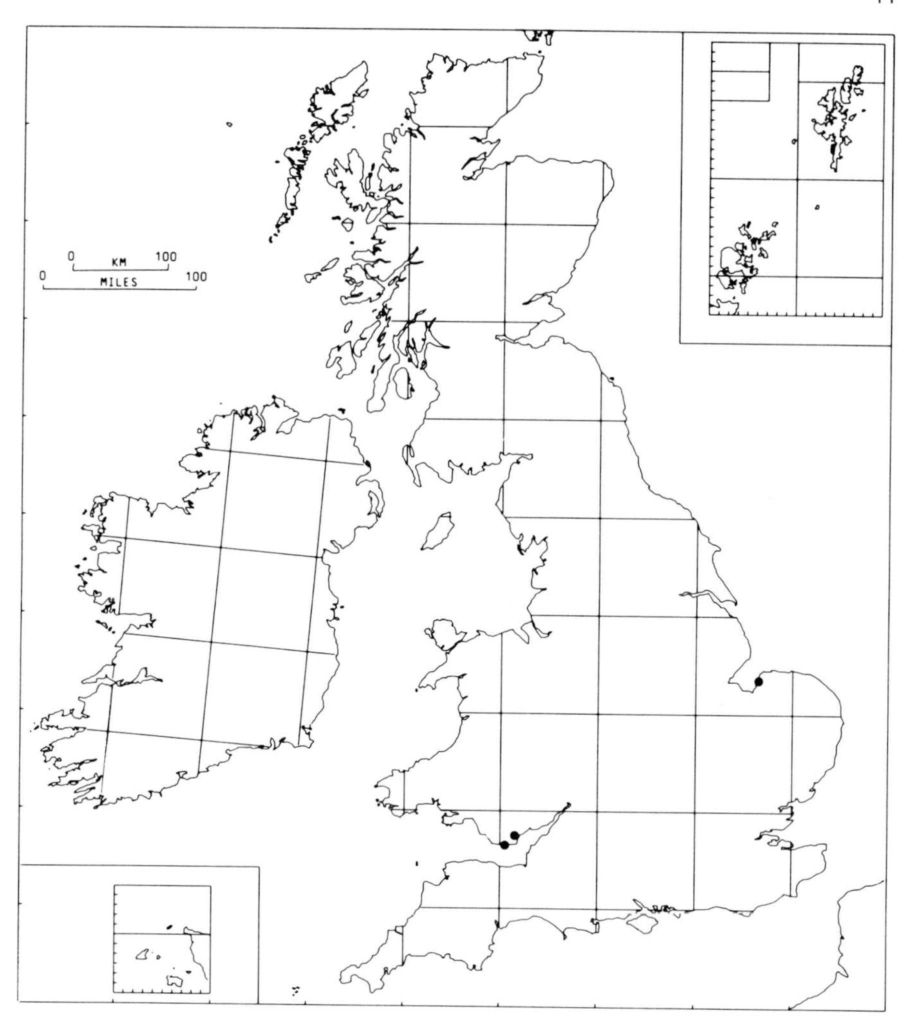

BUDDELUNDIELLA CATARACTAE

Number of records received: 5

England:	2 records
Wales:	3 records

Number of 10 km squares in which recorded:	3
Number of records with some habitat data:	5
Number of records from 1970 onwards:	5

HAPLOPHTHALMUS DANICUS Budde-Lund

This is a small (up to 4 mm) creamy or greyish white species which, with *H. mengei*, is easily distinguished in the field by the presence of numerous longitudinal ridges on the head and pereon. It is rarely very active and often remains immobile, in a slightly arched position, when disturbed. It is noticeably broader than *H. mengei* and lacks the prominent tubercles on pleonite 2.

Habitat data

A (145 records): Inland 77%, Coastal 23%.
B (145 records): Rural 62%, Suburban/village 30%, Urban 8%.
C (144 records): Open woodland 38%, Waste ground 17%, Garden 13%, Grassland (all types) 7%, Open scrubland 6%.
D (73 records). Roadside verge 38%, Compost/refuse heap 14%, Shore, etc, 14%.
E (146 records): Dead wood 56%, Litter 19%, Stones 8%.
H (a) Litter (and dead wood) (72 records): Mixed deciduous 38%, Other (mainly elm) 15%, Oak 14%, Beech 11%.
H (e) Soil (66 records): Clayey 41%, Loam 32%, Sandy 23%.
I (a) Location of animal, horizon (111 records): On ground surface 37%, In litter 31%, Less than 3 m above ground 23%, Less than 10 cm in soil 8%.

The map shows considerable collector bias in the clumping of records in south-east England. In this area, groups of records are attributable to a few recorders particularly experienced in finding the species. West of a line from the Solent to the Humber, records are sparse, but widely scattered. Attempts by experienced recorders to find *H. danicus* in apparently suitable sites to the west of this line have usually proved unsuccessful. The total absence of records from Somerset, Dorset, Wiltshire and most of Hampshire is perplexing, but is not a result of under-recording.

In south-east England it has been commonly recorded in woodland, often in association with fallen dead elms and clay or loam soils. This association was noted before the current epidemic of Dutch elm disease. Elm woodland in western England and Wales has been searched, but *H. danicus* has been recorded only rarely. The westernmost British record is from Boconnoc Park, East Cornwall, in a decaying beech. The northernmost recent record is from scrub and woodland at Thorpe le Street, South-East Yorkshire. Waste ground, gardens and roadside verges present a group of synanthropic habitats in which *H. danicus* has been recorded quite widely. Damp, but free-draining, friable soils, rich in humus, appear to be important at such sites. The few Irish records fit no general pattern and its apparent rarity cannot be explained.

H. danicus exhibits an ability to thrive and increase in numbers, over quite a short period, in a favourable habitat. It is only occasionally found as part of the 'background' fauna of an area, but in a favourable site it usually occurs in large numbers. It is possible that it is widespread, at least in the south, but occurs only in very small numbers and is usually detected only at particularly favourable, often temporary, sites which provide shelter and a source of food. The population ecology of this species would repay further study.

Vandel (1960a) described *H. danicus* as an '*espèce expansive*' (expansive or spreading species) having spread throughout Europe, and also to North Africa, Asia

Minor, several Atlantic islands, North America and Japan. Relating its distribution in France (common in Le Midi, the west and Corsica, but restricted to glasshouses, gardens and mines in the centre, north and east) to that known for the British Isles only compounds the puzzle.

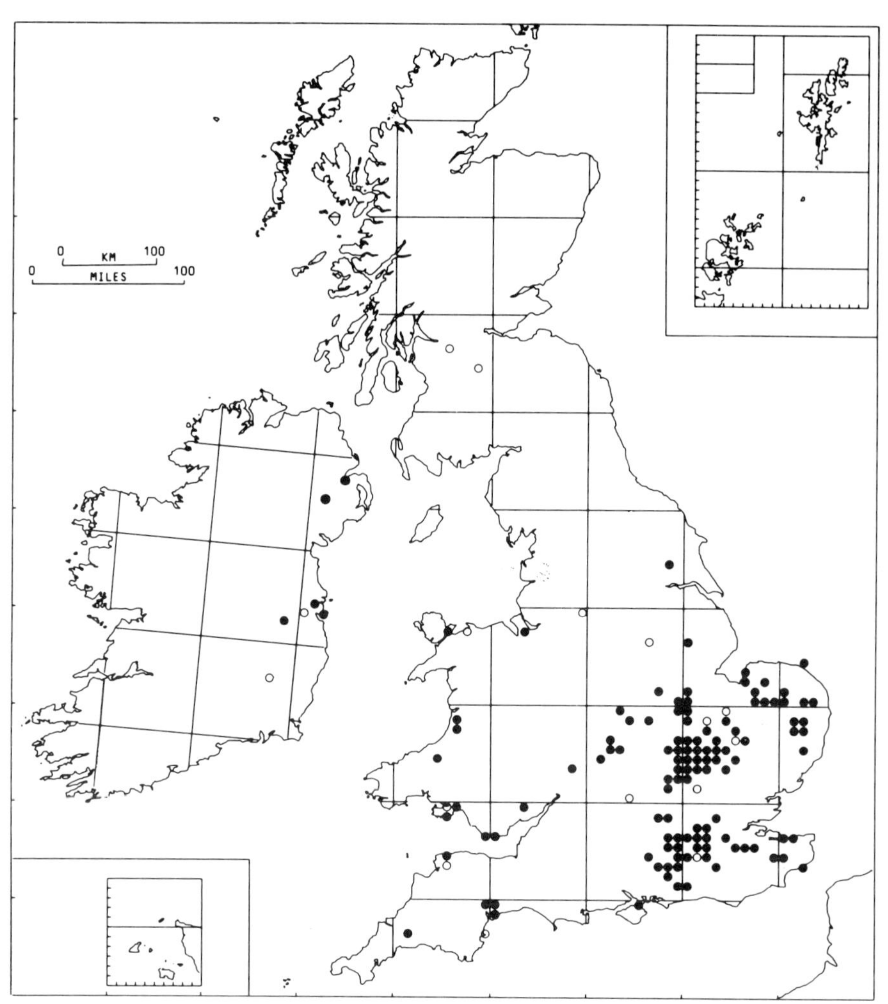

HAPLOPHTHALMUS DANICUS

Number of records received: 190

England:	162 records	(86%)	Ireland:	10 records	(5%)
Wales:	16 records	(9%)	Eire:	9 records	(5%)
Scotland:	2 records	(1%)	Northern Ireland:	1 record	(<1%)

Number of 10 km squares in which recorded: 135
Number (%) of records with some habitat data: 146 (77%)
Number (%) of records from 1970 onwards: 167 (88%)

HAPLOPHTHALMUS MENGEI (Zaddach)

Haplophthalmus mengei is a small (up to 4 mm) white or buff species which, like *Haplophthalmus danicus*, is readily distinguished from other small woodlice by the presence of numerous longitudinal ridges on the head and pereon. The presence of a pair of prominent tubercles on pleonite 2 and its narrow, elongate shape distinguish it from *H. danicus*. It is a sluggish species, often remaining immobile when disturbed.

Habitat data

A (260 records): Inland 52%, Coastal 48%.
B (260 records): Rural 89%, Suburban/village 9%, Urban 2%.
C (260 records): Grassland 30%, Woodland & Scrubland 22%, Sea & Estuary 16%, Waste ground 12%, Buildings, outside 5%, Gardens 4%.
D (144 records): Shore, etc, 21%, Roadside verge & Embankment/cutting 21%, Stabilised scree 13%, Natural cliff face 12%, Quarry floor 5%.
E (260 records): Stones 58%, Dead wood 13%, Soil/sand 10%, Litter 5%.
H (d) Soil/exposed rock (121 records): Calcareous 77%; Non-calcareous 23%.
I (a) Location of animal, horizon (144 records): Less than 10 cm in soil 42%, On ground surface 40%, In litter 12%.

H. mengei is essentially a soil species; the dominance of *stones* as a microsite reflects the commonest collecting technique, displacing stones embedded in soil. Sieving soil is also productive for this species, but is a comparatively little used technique. *H. mengei* is only rarely found under stones or dead wood on the surface of the ground. It is perhaps best to consider the Irish and British distributions separately.

The Irish distribution shows 4 patterns: (1) a circum-coastal distribution, where *H. mengei* occurs in the supralittoral zone, in soil under stones and in the deep litter of maritime vegetation; (2) on the shores and surrounding grasslands of calcareous lakes, particularly in Connaught (accounting for the large number of grassland records); (3) in soil and leaf litter of ash/hazel scrub woodland on the limestones of the Burren, Clare, in Sligo/Leitrim, and in Fermanagh; (4) in the central plain, where it is associated mainly with the sandy glacial soils of eskers and moraines, especially where these are undisturbed and calcareous. It seems to be genuinely scarce in the south-east where the soils are dry and non-calcareous.

In Britain, the scatter of records is sparser, but there is a similar coastal pattern, and groupings of inland records. Inland records are from (1) Carboniferous limestones of the Yorkshire Pennines, and (2) in the Trent valley and Bedfordshire on alluvial soils. There is also a scatter of records from Warwickshire across to East Anglia, mainly from valleys with deep alluvial soils or fen peat. There is clearly collector bias in the British distribution and it is badly under-recorded, but this species seems to be infrequent in south-east England.

In the British Isles, the distribution of this species may be dictated by the need for sufficient depth of calcareous friable soils and a high level of humidity.

The species known to British workers as *H. mengei* is believed to occur in western Europe, east to Austria and the Baltic coast of Poland (Legrand 1942, Dominiak 1961; Vandel 1960a, 1962). The variability of tergal sculpture, and minute differences in sexual characters, within the segregates of *H. mengei*, have not yet been adequately resolved.

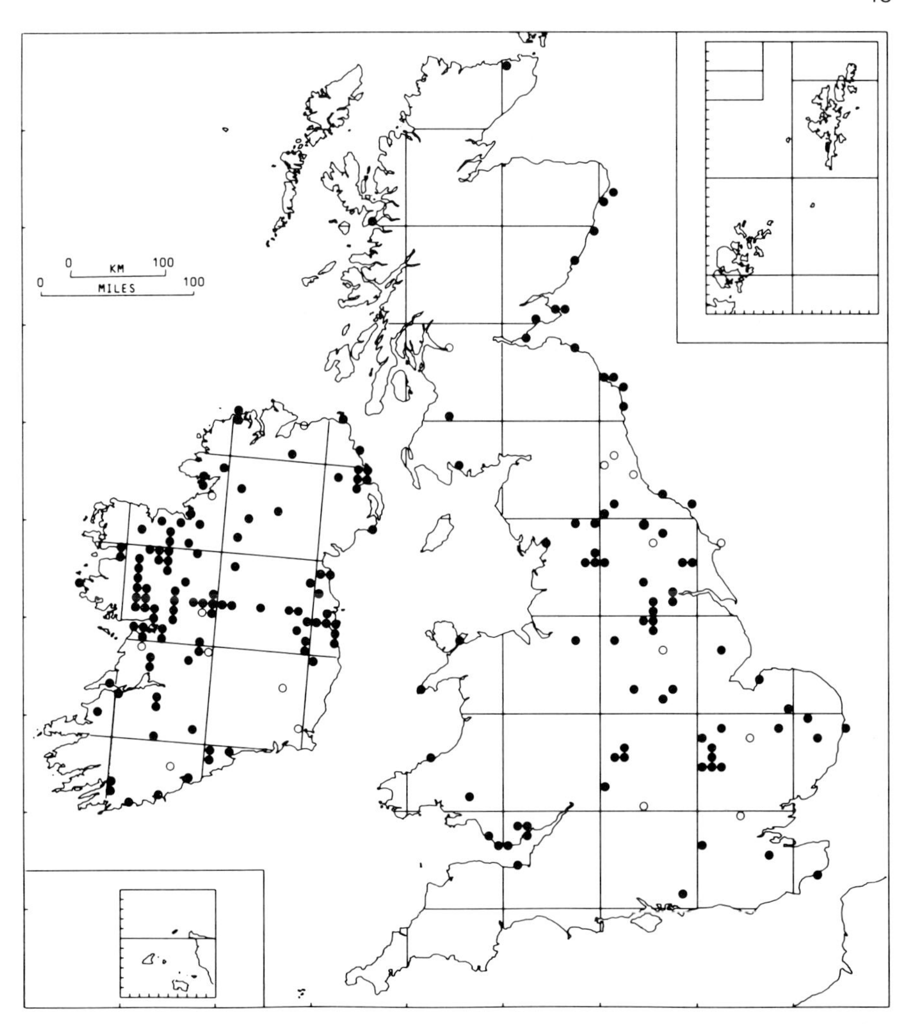

HAPLOPHTHALMUS MENGEI

Number of records received: 290

England:	91 records	(31%)
Wales:	37 records	(13%)
Scotland:	22 records	(8%)
Ireland:	140 records	(48%)
Eire:	127 records	(44%)
Northern Ireland:	13 records	(4%)

Number of 10 km squares in which recorded:	201	
Number (%) of records with some habitat data:	260	(90%)
Number (%) of records from 1970 onwards:	262	(90%)

METATRICHONISCOIDES CELTICUS Oliver & Trew

Metatrichoniscoides celticus is one of the smallest of British species, reaching only 3 mm in length. It is white in colour and is distinguishable in the field by the simple, tuberculous tergite sculpture (unlike *Haplophthalmus* spp.), the lack of eyes (unlike *Miktoniscus* spp. and some *Trichoniscoides* spp.), and the elongate body outline, pronounced lateral head projections and sluggish movements (unlike *Trichoniscoides* spp.). This species is known only from the British Isles and is confined to the supralittoral zone of rocky coasts, where it inhabits damp soils at depths of 5-20 cm.

M. celticus was first collected as recently as 1979, and the description appeared in 1981 (Oliver & Trew 1981). Perhaps because of the short history of this species, its known geographical range remains restricted to a 48 km stretch of the coastline of Glamorgan, south Wales. Surveys of apparently suitable sites in south-west England and Ireland have, however, failed to find it.

All records are from only 7 coastal sites and all second order habitats are classified as 'shore/water edge/strandline'. The habitat can be further defined as follows: all records occur in a zone some 5 m wide inland from the highest strandline at the top of rocky shores. In this zone, the vegetation and soil are subject to erosion. At 6 sites, the bedrock is limestone, and at the seventh, a calcareous conglomerate. The microsite has always been under deeply embedded stones, in damp soil, at depths of 5-20 cm. The association of soil and stone is very probably due to the hand-collecting method used, and the use of an extraction system may prove useful in further surveys. The soils on the limestone bedrock tend to be a heavy loam, but that overlying the conglomerate is a sandy loam. The covering vegetation is sparse, composed of coastal grassland species, predominantly *Festuca rubra*. The number of specimens found at any one time have been few (up to 6), despite considerable efforts. Visits to the type locality have not always yielded specimens, and it is suspected that this species is highly susceptible to changes in soil conditions, such as humidity, which result in the animals moving deep into the soil during dry conditions, where they are more difficult to collect. Species associated with *M. celticus* are, in order of frequency, *Haplophthalmus mengei, Trichoniscoides saeroeensis, Trichoniscus pygmaeus* and *Androniscus dentiger*. This sequence is close to that of the general frequency of occurrence of these species in soil habitats in the supralittoral zone, and no significant pattern of association is yet apparent.

The extreme restriction of the geographical and ecological ranges of *M. celticus* could imply a possible need for conservation measures (see Appendix 6). The sites are at present subject to only slight human disturbance; major pollution or industrial development could also affect this species. The small number of sites known may reflect the difficulty in collecting this species, rather than its true rarity.

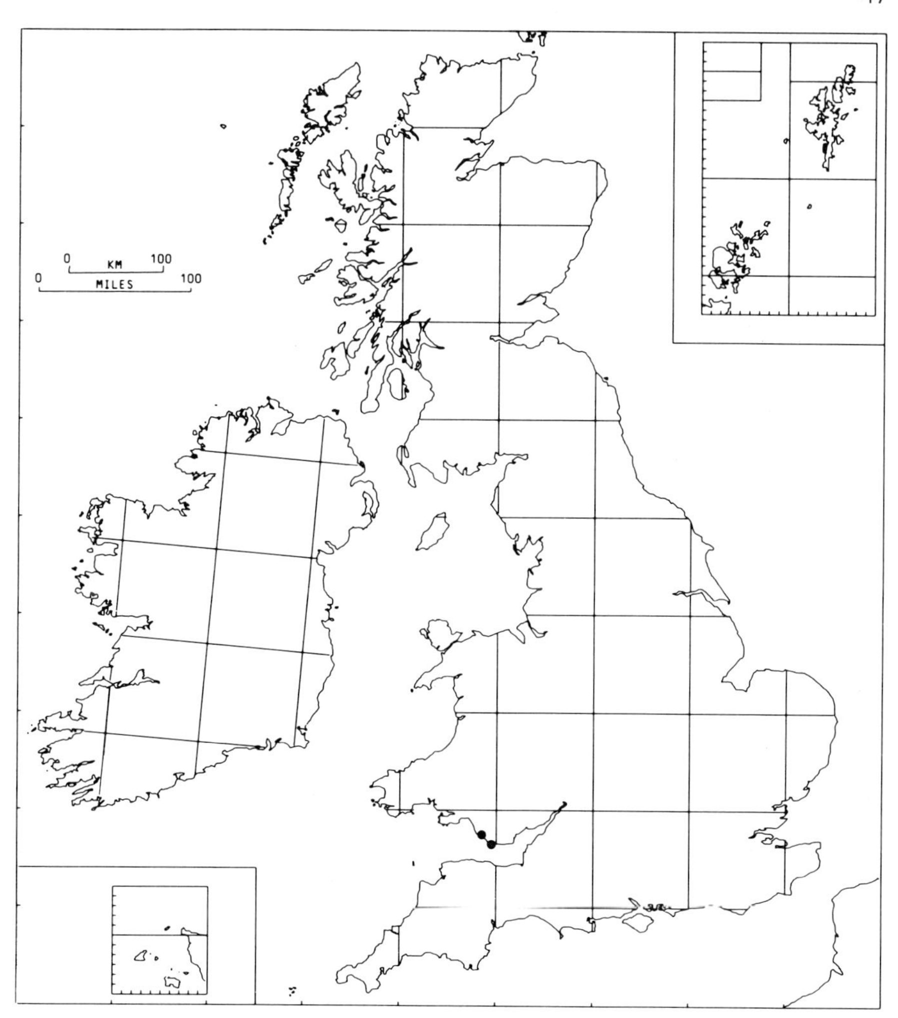

METATRICHONISCOIDES CELTICUS

Number of records received: 8

Wales: 8 records

Number of 10 km squares in which recorded: 2
Number of records with some habitat data: 8
Number of records from 1970 onwards: 8

MIKTONISCUS PATIENCEI Vandel

This small (4 mm), white, trichoniscid woodlouse is readily distinguishable from other species in the family by the coarsely tuberculate dorsal surface and the eyes which are composed of a single large black ocellus. *Miktoniscus patiencei* is restricted to the supralittoral zone, where it inhabits deep litter, friable soils and shingles at, and above, the strandlines of salt marshes and sea cliffs.

M. patiencei was first recognized as a species new to the British Isles in 1976, when it was collected, quite independently, on consecutive days, in salt marshes on the Isle of Wight and on a sea cliff in East Cornwall. A single female collected in 1971 on the Medway estuary, West Kent, had remained unidentified. Since the presence of this species in the British Isles was established, it has been recorded widely along the English Channel and the southern coast of Ireland. In their review of this species, Oliver and Sutton (1982) concluded that it might have a restricted southerly distribution, but a population was found on the Kincardineshire coast in 1982, suggesting a wider distribution.

Three recognizable habitats are occupied by *M. patiencei*. In salt marshes, it occurs, often in large numbers, in the damp layer of deep grass litter, in friable soil and amongst roots of upper salt marsh vegetation, typified by species of the genera *Elymus, Juncus* and *Halimione*. On sea cliffs, the vertical range is greater, from the strandline to a height of 40 m, where *M. patiencei* inhabits the friable soil and litter of dense vegetation typified by the grass *Festuca rubra*. On stable shingle shores, the microsite is at, and just above, the extreme high water mark of spring tides where, at depths of approximately 10 cm, a layer of rotting seaweed and humus accumulates. Sparse vegetation frequently covers these shores and includes *Beta vulgaris maritima, Atriplex* sp. and *Sonchus asper*. On shingle shores, *M. patiencei* often occurs with *Trichoniscoides saeroeensis* and in similar numbers, but in salt marshes *M. patiencei* is often more numerous than *T. saeroeensis*.

M. patiencei is recorded from the Channel coast of France and Brittany (Vandel 1960a). A single record from Madeira (Vandel 1960b) may be this species, but confusion with another 4, more southerly, species may have occurred (Oliver & Sutton 1982).

[In 1983 A O Chater recorded a second locality for *M. patiencei* on the Kincardineshire coast.]

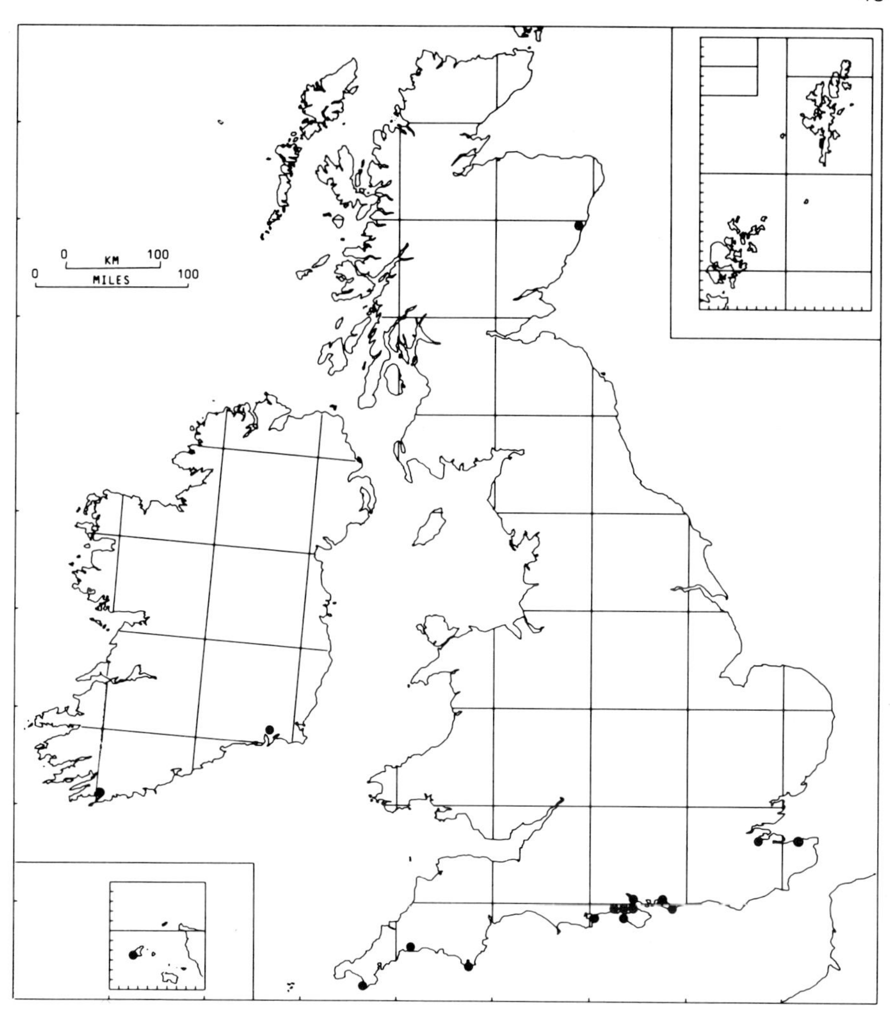

MIKTONISCUS PATIENCEI

Number of records received: 22

England:	14 records
Scotland:	1 record
Channel Islands:	2 records
Ireland:	5 records
Eire:	5 records

Number of 10 km squares in which recorded:	16
Number of records with some habitat data:	16
Number of records from 1970 onwards:	22

ORITONISCUS FLAVUS (Budde-Lund)

In life, *Oritoniscus flavus* most closely resembles an exceptionally large specimen of *Trichoniscus pusillus*, being often 8 mm or more in length. Adult specimens may be recognized in the field by their characteristic purple-maroon colouration (much darker than *T. pusillus*) and rapid movements. They have a wet, shining, appearance and the broad head and constricted pleon give a distinctive tapering outline reminiscent of a trilobite. The eye is also distinctive, composed of a single large ocellus, unlike *T. pusillus* which has 3 separate ocelli. When preserved in alcohol, specimens rapidly lose their distinctive colouration, which fades through carrot to yellow and presumably explains the unlikely specific epithet *flavus* (yellow). It is a very agile species, difficult to capture and examine.

Habitat data

A (44 records): Inland 82%, Coastal 18%.
B (44 records): Rural 86%, Suburban/village 12%, Urban 2%.
C (44 records): Woodland 18%, Waste ground 18%, Grassland, ungrazed 16%, Grassland, grazed 11%, Scrubland, open with herbs/grass 11%.
E (43 records): Stones 40%, Dead wood 21%, Shingle 14%.

Its distribution in Ireland is not particularly associated with the coast, or with synanthropic sites, although it may often be found in ruined buildings and rubbish, where these occur near rivers. Field experience indicates that it requires microsites with high humidity (eg stabilized leaf litter). In almost all cases, it was encountered close (ie less than 20 m) to a river bank (or associated land drains), often where regular flooding and alluvial enrichment occurred. It can be difficult to locate during extended dry spells, but can be found under stones and in river gravel, also under rotting vegetation.

For many years, *O. flavus* was thought to occur in Ireland only in the south-east. However, the species has recently been found in the vicinity of Limerick, on the River Shannon, on the River Liffey near Lucan, Dublin, and in Meath on the River Boyne, west of Slane. It is abundant at the latter site, its most northerly known locality in the world.

O. flavus is a biogeographical curiosity. It is unknown in Britain, but is widespread in south and east Ireland, occurring in 13 vice-counties. Its European distribution, centred on the Pyrenees, has led to claims that it is another example of the 'Lusitanian' element within the Irish fauna. That it is so widespread in Ireland, but not in Britain, is puzzling. Unlike many introductions, it infrequently occurs in synanthropic sites. It may be a genuine Lusitanian species, or possibly a species that once lived in Britain and has subsequently died out. Its recent discovery in Dublin and Meath may indicate a continued expansion of its range, or merely be the result of increased recording. More detailed surveys, and monitoring of the peripheral colonies, could provide valuable insight into the status of this species.

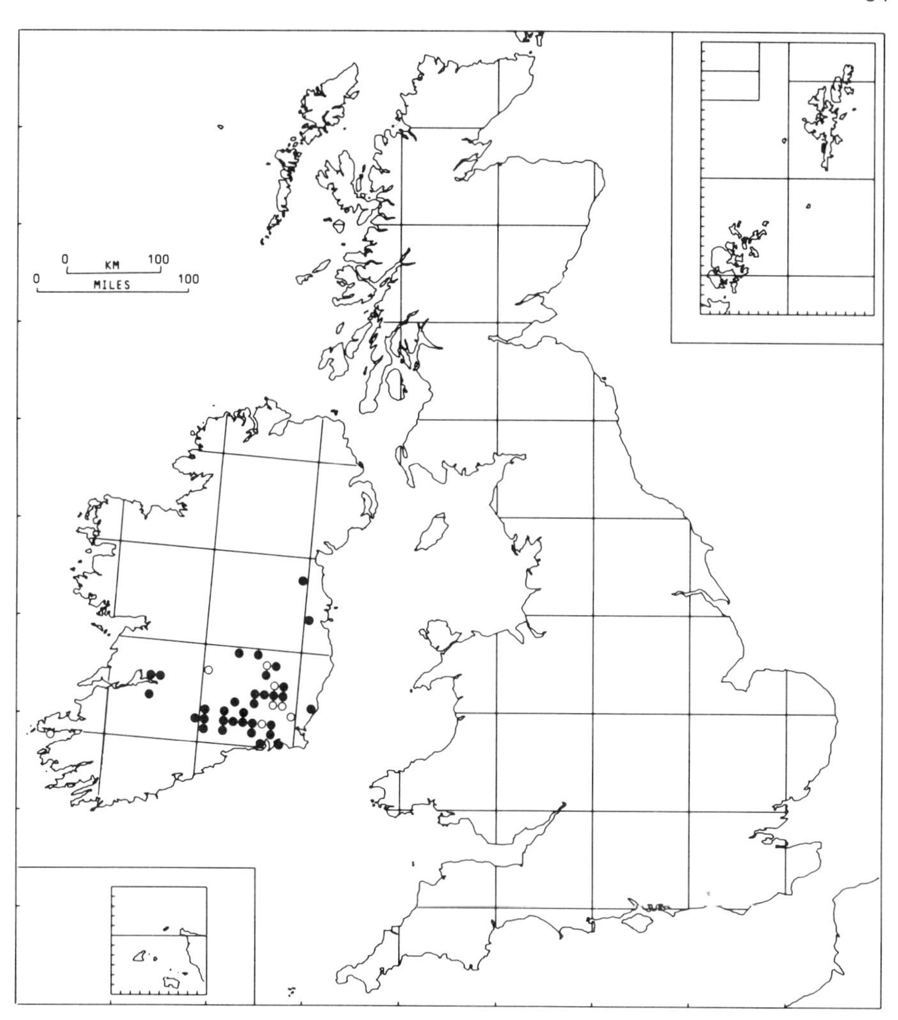

ORITONISCUS FLAVUS

Number of records received: 55

Ireland:	55 records	(100%)
Eire:	55 records	(100%)

Number of 10 km squares in which recorded:	41	
Number (%) of records with some habitat data:	44	(80%)
Number (%) of records from 1970 onwards:	43	(78%)

TRICHONISCOIDES ALBIDUS (Budde-Lund)

In life, *Trichoniscoides albidus* resembles a small, dull *Trichoniscus pusillus*, a species with which it usually occurs. *T. albidus* is reddish-purple in colour, but this colouring is lost rapidly in alcohol to leave an off-white colour, hence the specific epithet *albidus* (whitish). *T. pusillus* retains its colour in alcohol. *T. albidus* is densely covered with small tubercles, which give the dorsal surface a matt-finish appearance, unlike the shiny surface of *T. pusillus*.

T. albidus was quite widely recorded up to the 1940s (Collinge 1943b), but many of these records are believed to be mis-identifications or nomenclatural confusions. For example, many of the old records from Ireland seem to refer to *Trichoniscoides saeroeensis*. Preserved material in museum collections supporting some of these earlier records is in such a poor state of preservation as to be unidentifiable. Only one early record (from Alnwick, Cheviot, in about 1911) has been confirmed by reference to museum material.

Recent records show marked bias resulting from the activities of a few recorders experienced in sampling for this species. Most noticeable is the Bedfordshire area, where A J Rundle has recorded it widely, mainly by searching under bricks, rubble, etc, and by sieving wet soil in ditches and on river and stream banks, particularly at the sides of culverts. He has sampled many of these, often unappetising, sites during his detailed tetrad (2 km × 2 km square) survey of the county. The alluvial loamy soils of Bedfordshire may be particularly favourable for *T. albidus*. The application of similar collecting methods elsewhere has resulted in only a thin scatter of records in eastern England, from Robin Hood's Bay, North-east Yorkshire, south to sites in Berkshire, Surrey and East Kent.

It has been recorded from 2 localities in Ireland, under stones on a roadside verge near Durrow, Laois, and under stones in a long disused garden at The Strawberry Beds in the Liffey valley, near Lucan, Dublin.

Only 22 records included habitat data, too small a sample for any clear analysis of habitat preferences. It is a soil-dwelling species usually recorded in wet (sometimes waterlogged) friable loamy soils in ditches, beside watercourses, on sea cliffs and also from peat soils in fens. It is certainly under-recorded in Britain and may occur widely where suitable soil conditions occur. Its status in Ireland is uncertain; many apparently suitable sites have been examined but, although 2 species with which it is frequently associated, *Haplophthalmus mengei* and *Trichoniscus pygmaeus*, are common, *T. albidus* has not been found.

T. albidus has been recorded from western France, Belgium, the Netherlands, the Rhineland of West Germany, Denmark and Scania in Sweden. Vandel (1960a) stated that, in France, it occurs in damp forests and on sea coasts. He considered that it is adapted to a cold Atlantic climate.

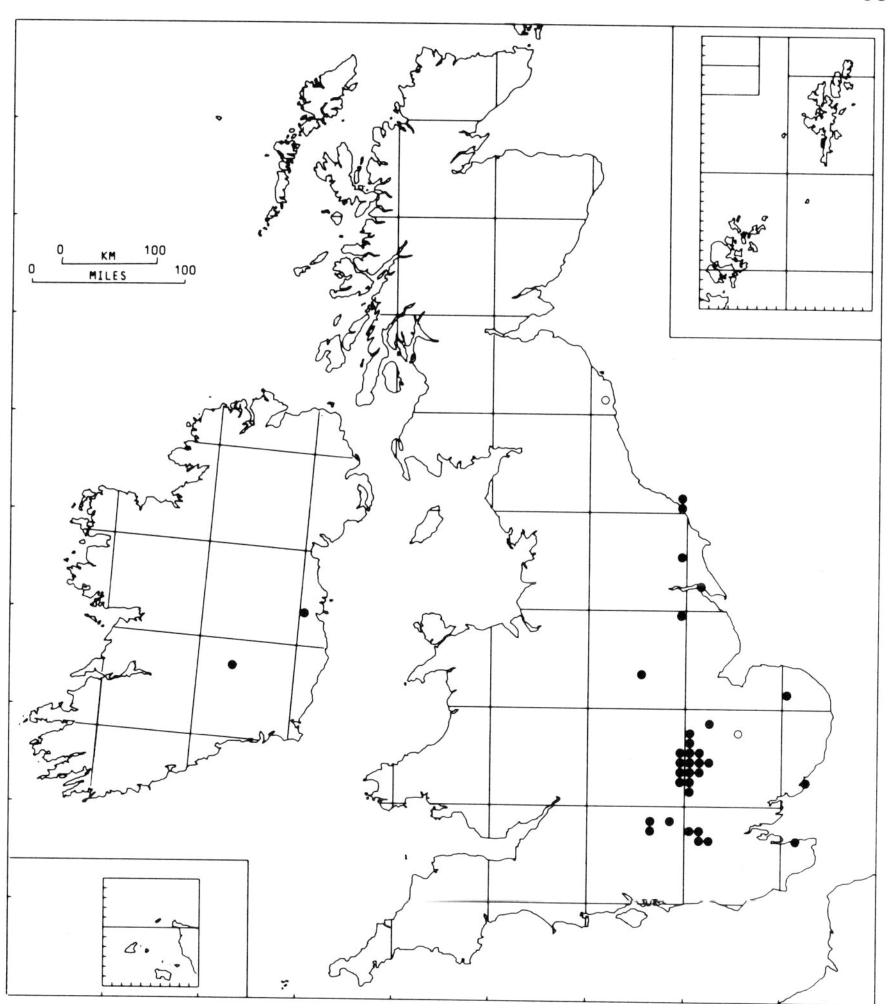

TRICHONISCOIDES ALBIDUS

Number of records received: 50

England:	47 records	(94%)
Ireland:	3 records	(6%)
Eire:	3 records	(6%)

Number of 10 km squares in which recorded:	36	
Number (%) of records with some habitat data:	22	(44%)
Number (%) of records from 1970 onwards:	48	(96%)

TRICHONISCOIDES SAEROEENSIS Lohmander

Trichoniscoides saeroeensis can be distinguished from most other small white trichoniscids by its apparent smoothness, the bright red/pink ocelli and the pink colouration of the pleon, the pereion being creamy white. These characters are distinctive in the field, but occasionally specimens may lack any colouration, and in alcohol all colouration is rapidly lost. *T. saeroeensis* is coastal in distribution, inhabiting soil and shingle in a variety of habitats, from rocky strandlines, through salt marshes to coastal woodland, but there are isolated records from caves and mines which are not easily reconciled with our present knowledge of the habitat of this species. Similar coastal species are *Miktoniscus patiencei*, which is a dead-white colour with black ocelli; *Metatrichoniscoides celticus*, which lacks ocelli, has an elongate body outline, pronounced lateral head projections and is sluggish; and *Haplophthalmus mengei*, which has distinctive tergal sculpturing.

T. saeroeensis was first recorded from the British Isles in 1966, from a disused mine at Warton, West Lancashire, and in 1968 it was found in caves in the Burren, Clare (Sheppard 1968). The species had been found, but mis-identified, in Ireland in 1913 (Doogue & Harding 1982) and in Scotland in 1934 (Collinge 1942b; Harding 1977). Subsequent records have been made in coastal woodland in Kirkcudbrightshire and a strandline in Harris, Outer Hebrides. Concerted efforts in the late 1970s indicated that this species was frequent, if searched for carefully, in the supralittoral zone. The total number of records received to date, although relatively small, is sufficient to indicate a wide coastal distribution for this species throughout the British Isles.

Habitat data

A (65 records): Coastal 100%.
B (65 records): Rural 94%, Suburban/village 6%.
C (65 records): Sea 63%, Estuary 8%, Salt marsh 6%, Woodland, open with herbs/grass 6%, Grassland 5%.
D (47 records): Shore, etc, 83%, Natural cliff face 11%.
E (65 records): Stones 48%, Soil/sand 23%, Shingle 12%, Dead wood 5%.
F (b) Shore (51 records): Splash zone 73%, Between splash zone and 100 m 27%.
I (a) Location of animal, horizon (44 records): Less than 10 cm in soil 55%, More than 10 cm in soil 25%, On ground surface 11%, In litter 9%.

T. saeroeensis is essentially a supralittoral isopod of the soil or deep litter. At east coast sites and in south Wales, it is generally found by searching in shingle and under stones, from the extreme high water mark to 5 m above high water mark. The vegetation cover is usually sparse, and the soils are thin and lack humus. On west coasts and at Irish sites, *T. saeroeensis* has a wider vertical range and is also found in salt marshes, storm beaches and coastal grassland, where it inhabits the deep layers of litter at, and above, the high water mark. In these western regions, with Atlantic weather, suitable conditions may well extend slightly further inland. On the map, the apparently inland records in southern Ireland are from estuarine sites.

T. saeroeensis is often quite abundant once the exact microsite has been traced. It is often the dominant small isopod in suitable conditions and has been found with *H. mengei*, *Trichoniscus pygmaeus*, *M. patiencei* and *M. celticus*. At British sites, supralittoral amphipods are often found in association. Elsewhere, *T. saeroeensis* is known from the coasts of southern Sweden, Denmark and Brittany.

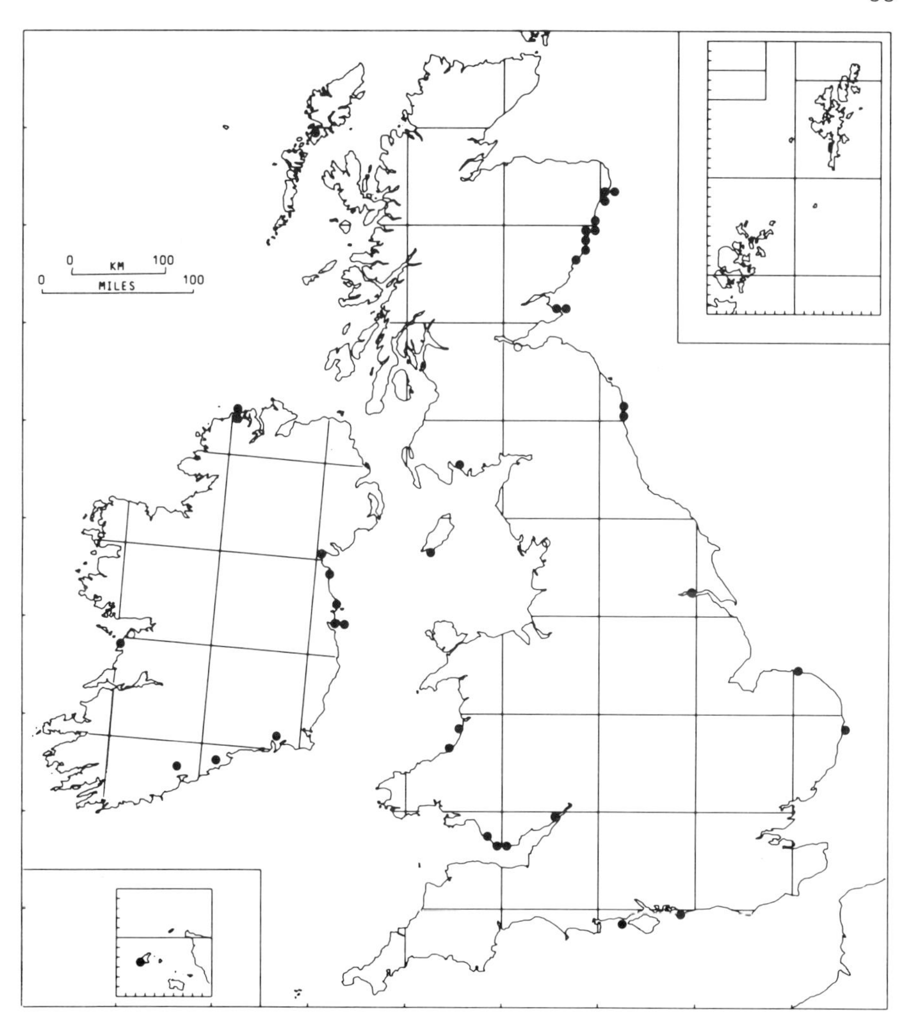

TRICHONISCOIDES SAEROEENSIS

Number of records received: 74

England:	11 records	(15%)
Wales:	15 records	(20%)
Scotland:	24 records	(33%)
Isle of Man:	1 record	(1%)
Channel Islands:	2 records	(3%)
Ireland:	21 records	(28%)
Eire:	21 records	(28%)

Number of 10 km squares in which recorded:	42	
Number (%) of records with some habitat data:	65	(88%)
Number (%) of records from 1970 onwards:	68	(92%)

TRICHONISCOIDES SARSI (Patience)

Trichoniscoides sarsi is similar in appearance to *Trichoniscoides saeroeensis*. It is a clean, white colour, usually with striking pink or orange patches at the hind end on either side of the central line. The ocelli are also pink or orange-coloured. The 2 species have been confused in the past and several published records of *T. sarsi* are, in fact, of *T. saeroeensis*. On present evidence, *T. sarsi* is mainly an inland species, whereas *T. saeroeensis* is coastal.

The thin scatter of definite records provides no clear indication of habitat preferences other than that *T. sarsi* is a soil-dwelling species, in common with other species of this genus. The early published records have been discounted because of known errors in identification and nomenclatural confusions. Records from Britain have been from grassland and screes, particularly on chalk. The Irish records have been from long neglected gardens near Dublin city. At Barton Hills in Bedfordshire, *T. sarsi* was extracted from shallow turf and soil samples using Tullgren funnels. The samples were of chalk downland turf in a fenced area, from which rabbits and grazing stock had been excluded. At Diddling Hill, West Sussex, it has been collected by hand on 2 occasions from a fan of chalk rubble scree on a steep, north-facing slope in scrubby chalk grassland, and at Noar Hill, North Hampshire, it was sieved from soil in 2 hollows on chalk downland. At Wye, East Kent, it was found in soil amongst rubbish next to garden and churchyard walls.

One notable feature of some records made when *T. sarsi* has been collected by hand at or near the soil surface has been the temperature. Some records have been made in cold and wet conditions, even frosty weather, which is unusual for such a small species which might be expected to avoid cold or freezing conditions. At one site in Dublin city, it was collected among ice crystals under a stone. In these cold conditions, it has appeared to be quite plentiful and usually active, unlike other species in the vicinity.

T. sarsi has been recorded in western France, Denmark, Sweden and Norway. It has also been recorded from Newfoundland, probably as an introduction.

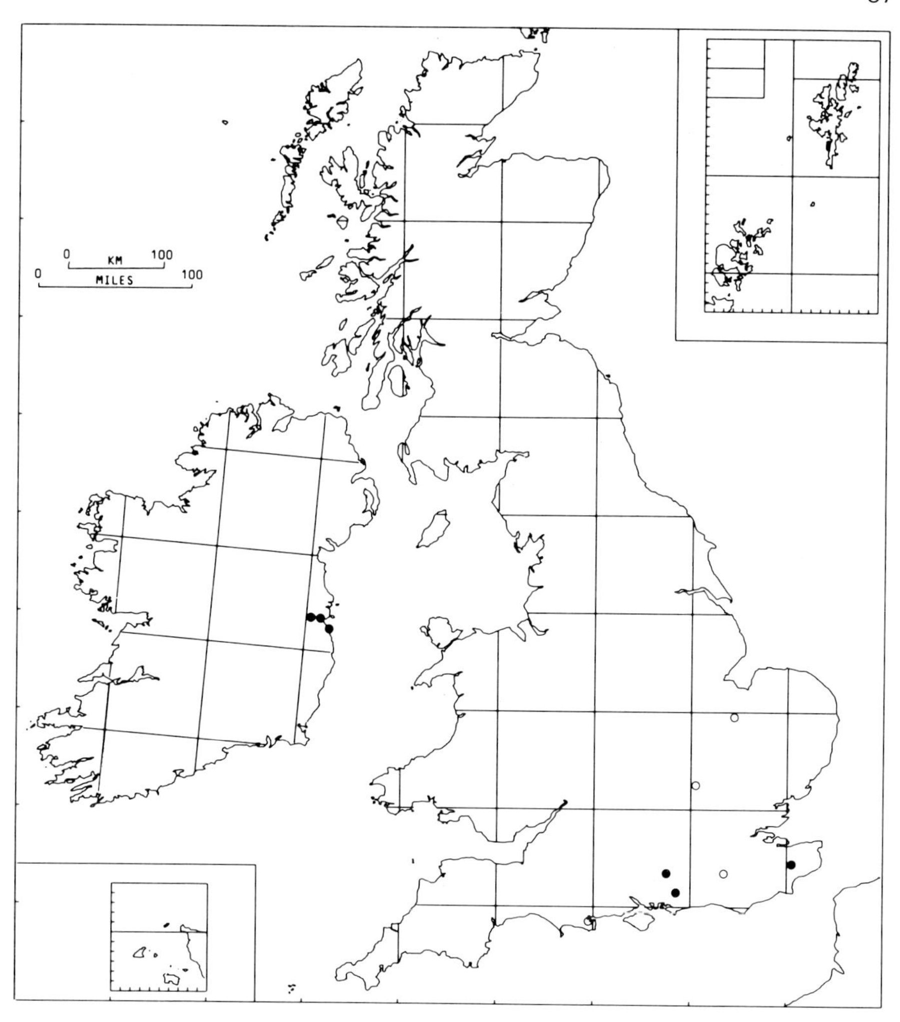

TRICHONISCOIDES SARSI

Number of records received: 15

England:	10 records
Ireland:	5 records
Eire:	5 records

Number of 10 km squares in which recorded:	10
Number of records with some habitat data:	11
Number of records from 1970 onwards:	10

TRICHONISCUS PUSILLUS Brandt

This is the commonest small woodlouse in the British Isles but, because of its size, it is overlooked by inexperienced collectors. It is instantly recognizable by its shiny, reddish-brown appearance, while closer inspection reveals a white mottling which results from the attachment of muscles on to the dorsal surface. Male *Trichoniscus pusillus* are often darker than females, and have distinctive white patches on the pleon segments where the muscles of their genital apparatus are attached (Frankel 1973). A violet-coloured variety (*violaceus* Schöbl) is occasionally encountered.

Ecologically, *T. pusillus* is versatile, being very mobile and able to occupy a wide range of habitats (Lloyd 1963; Sutton 1968). It is ubiquitous throughout the length and breadth of the British Isles. In many habitats it is the most abundant species, often reaching densities of thousands per m^2. The species has been recorded from virtually every habitat and microsite covered by the survey.

Habitat data

A (3575 records): Inland 66%, Coastal 34%.
B (3569 records): Rural 81%, Suburban/village 16%, Urban 3%.
C (3573 records): Woodland, open with herbs/grass 17%, Woodland, other 17%, Waste ground 14%, Grassland, grazed 12%, Grassland, ungrazed 7%, Garden 6%, Scrub, open with herbs/grass 6%.
D (1766 records): Roadside verge 24%, Shore, etc. 10%, Embankment 9%, Walls 8%, Screes 8%, Quarries 8%.
E (3557 records): Stones 35%, Dead wood 23%, Litter 21%, Human rubbish/ garbage 5%.
H (d) Soil/exposed rock (1627 records): Non-calcareous 51%, Calcareous 49%.
H (e) Soil (1551 records): Loam 46%, Clayey 27%, Sandy 17%, Peat 6%.
I (a) Location of animal, horizon (2587 records): On ground surface 55%, In litter 29%, Less than 3 m above ground 8%, Less than 10 cm in soil 7%.

Interpretation of the distribution and ecology of *T. pusillus* in Britain is complicated by the presence of 2 reproductively isolated forms, *T. pusillus* f. *pusillus* Brandt and *T. pusillus* f. *provisorius* Racovitza. The occurrence of these 2 forms was studied in co-operation with the survey. Taken as a whole, *T. pusillus* is widespread throughout Europe and North America.

There have been several ecological studies of *T. pusillus* in Britain, both as a species and as the 2 forms. Standen, née Healey (Healey 1963; Standen 1970, 1973) studied f. *pusillus* in woodland, mostly in Cheshire, concentrating mainly on its life history and annual production. Sutton (1966, 1968, 1970) described the population dynamics and growth patterns of f. *pusillus* in limestone grassland at Wytham, Berkshire, and Phillipson (1983), in beech woodland at the same site, examined the life cycle, numbers and biomass of f. *provisorius*. Frankel (1976) examined the taxonomic status, biology and ecology of the species in Epping Forest, South Essex, paying special attention (Frankel 1979a, b) to the juvenile stadia and growth patterns of both forms. Subsequent work on the 2 forms by Fussey is summarized in the following account (pages 60-61) of the forms of *T. pusillus*. Frankel, Sutton and Fussey (1981) collaborated to summarize their research on the sex ratios of the 2 forms.

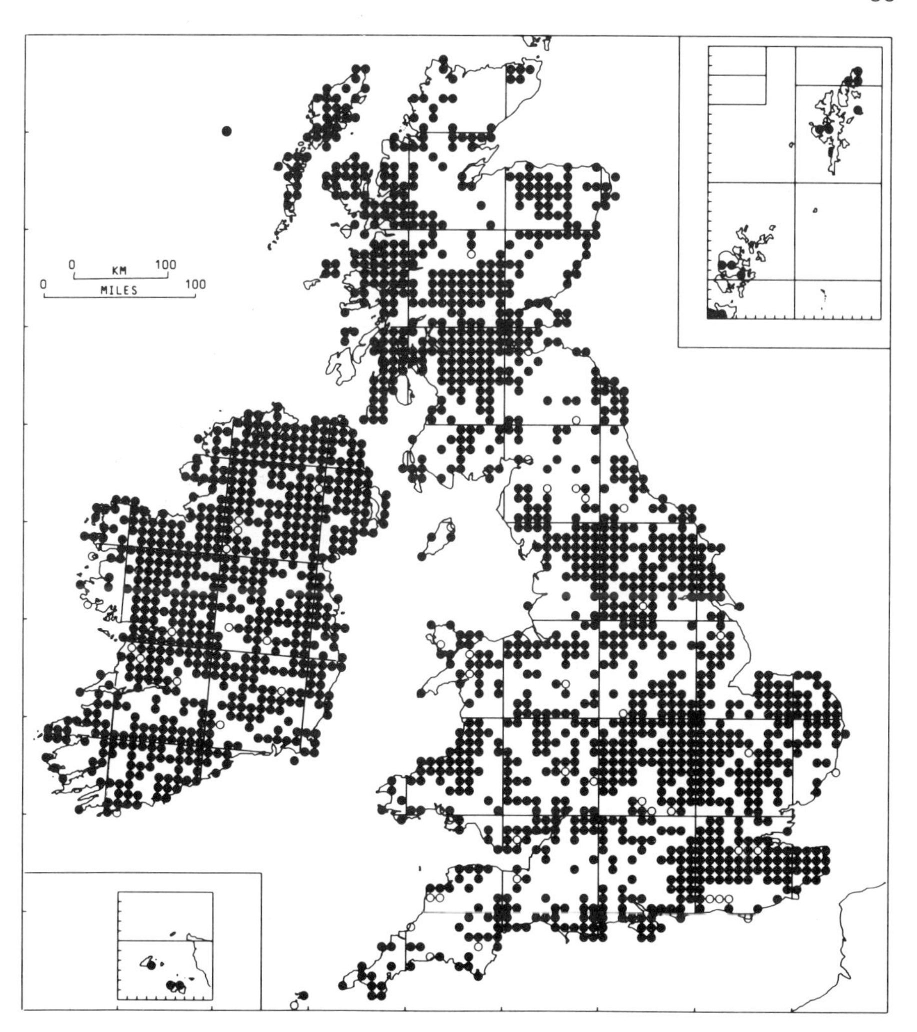

TRICHONISCUS PUSILLUS

Number of records received: 3974

England:	1988 records (50%)	Channel Islands:	5 records (<1%)
Wales:	239 records (6%)	Ireland:	1013 records (26%)
Scotland:	723 records (18%)	Eire:	810 records (21%)
Isle of Man:	6 records (<1%)	Northern Ireland:	203 records (5%)

Number of 10 km squares in which recorded: 2047
Number (%) of records with some habitat data: 3573 (90%)
Number (%) of records from 1970 onwards: 3765 (95%)

TRICHONISCUS PUSILLUS form *PUSILLUS* Brandt and form *PROVISORIUS* Racovitza

In Britain, *Trichoniscus pusillus* is represented by 2 forms: *T. pusillus* f. *pusillus* Brandt 1833 is parthenogenetic and composed almost exclusively of females, while *T. pusillus* f. *provisorius* Racovitza 1908 is gonochoristic and has been shown to have males and females in more or less equal numbers (Frankel *et al.* 1981). Although they were previously referred to as subspecies by Legrand, Strouhal and Vandel (1950), the term *form* is preferred here as no interbreeding is possible between them.

The 2 forms are morphologically very similar and the fact that f. *pusillus* tends to be approximately 15% longer (Frankel 1979b) is of no use in discriminating between the 2 forms in a continuously growing and moulting crustacean. Formerly, identification of the 2 forms relied on a difference in shape of the exopodite of the first male pleopod (Edney 1953; Sutton 1972), but microscopic examination of the genitalia is a delicate operation and few records resulted. A further drawback is that male f. *pusillus* only occur at a frequency of about 1% in pure populations (Gruner 1966) and so, in consequence, f. *provisorius* was over-recorded in relation to f. *pusillus*.

To gain more information on the occurrence of the 2 forms a sub-scheme was set up, as part of the survey, in 1978. Populations were assessed statistically for the presence of the 2 forms by using the sex ratios of numerically large samples taken from small discrete microsites (a precaution against sampling more than one population at a time). Pure f. *pusillus* populations have few, if any, males while pure f. *provisorius* populations have intermediate sex ratios. G D Fussey sampled many sites, other members of the survey contributed specimens or records, and previous data from V Standen and S L Sutton were also included to give information from 109 sites in Britain and 30 sites in Ireland. The results were analysed by Fussey (Fussey & Sutton 1981; Fussey 1984). The proportions of the 2 forms at these sites are shown on the map opposite (○ f. *pusillus*, ● f. *provisorius*).

Previous work on other animal species with parthenogenetic forms led former researchers to suppose that f. *pusillus* might well replace f. *provisorius* at more northerly locations (Sutton 1972). The present study shows that, in the British Isles, no simple correlation is apparent between the proportions of the 2 forms and latitude. Analysis of habitat data shows a close association of f. *provisorius* with areas where the soil/exposed rock type is *Calcareous*. *T. pusillus* is a species with a very broad niche and there are clearly many factors influencing its distribution. Nevertheless, analysis suggests that it is the physical factors of calcareous habitats (their tendency to be well drained and, where vegetation is sparse, to warm up rapidly with insolation) which account for this association, rather than the chemical factors (pH and presence of calcium carbonate). To this extent, f. *provisorius* might best be considered as a thermophile rather than as a calciphile *per se*. A typical habitat for f. *provisorius* would be a south-facing rock scree or a karst pavement.

The distribution of the 2 forms in Europe and North America has yet to be methodically surveyed, and, until sex ratio data become available, interpretation is not easy. Records of f. *pusillus* range from Sardinia to Norway and Finland, and from Poland in the east to Iceland, Newfoundland and the USA in the west. There are records of f. *provisorius* from Poland, Turkey and Lebanon in the east and Algeria in the south. Large numbers have recently been found at 2 sites in Denmark, corresponding with the most northerly record in Britain, at 56° 30′ N. Further north, f. *provisorius* has been recorded in a heated glasshouse near Helsinki, Finland (Palmén 1947). It seems that f. *pusillus* does have a more northerly range while, conversely, f. *provisorius* extends further south. The ranges may well be determined in some part by levels of insolation. There is a considerable overlap in their distributions (in the British Isles, for example) and there are many questions still to be answered on the ecology of the 2 forms.

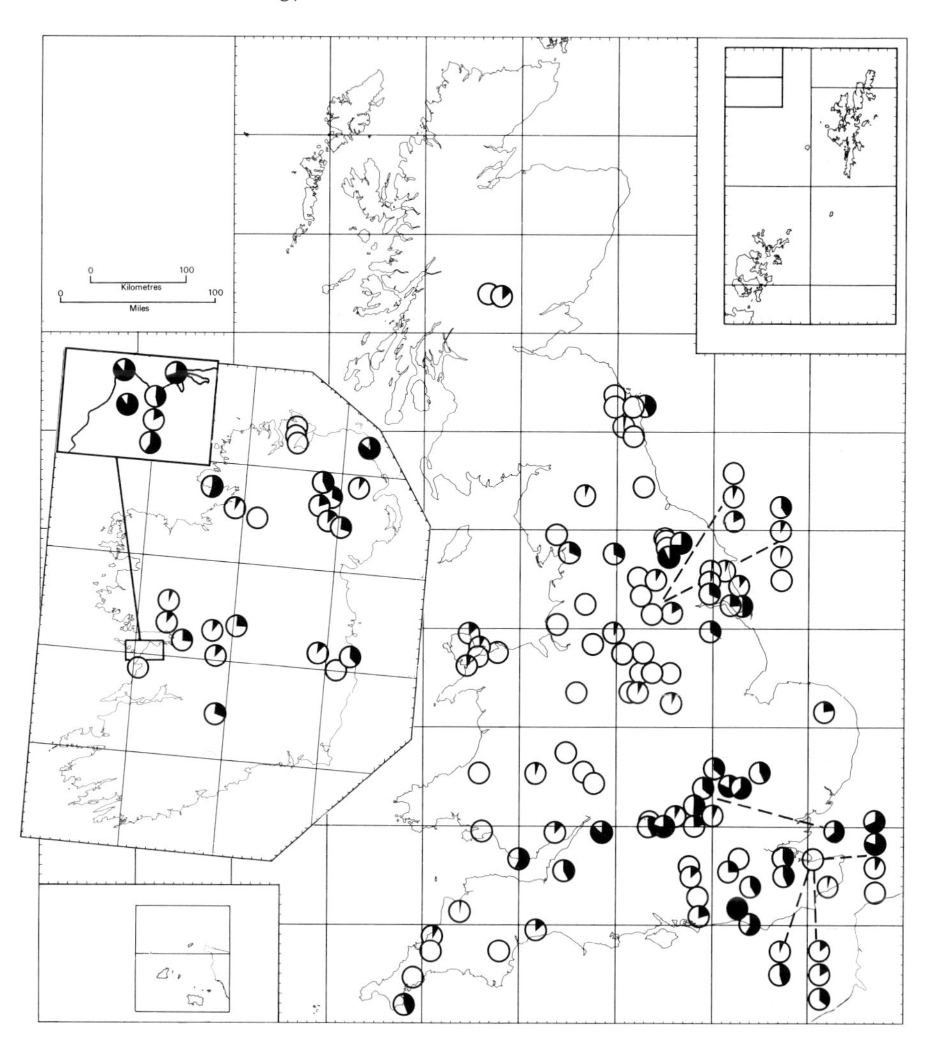

TRICHONISCUS PUSILLUS forms

TRICHONISCUS PYGMAEUS Sars

Trichoniscus pygmaeus is a very small, off-white, rather slow-moving species which lives in the soil, under embedded stones and in the deeper layers of leaf litter. It is easily confused with the unpigmented young of *Trichoniscus pusillus*, but is more elongate and virtually lacks pigmentation on the head. Mature males are no bigger than immature (unpigmented) *T. pusillus*. This may be the most under-recorded of our British species, owing to its deep-dwelling habit and the ease with which it is mistaken for juvenile *T. pusillus*.

Habitat data

A (487 records): Inland 69%, Coastal 31%.
B (485 records): Rural 73%, Suburban/village 22%, Urban 5%.
C (484 records): Grassland, lightly grazed & ungrazed 22%, Waste ground 20%, Woodland 19%, Garden 11%, Building, outside 9%.
D (286 records): Roadside verge 21%, Shore, etc, 11%, Quarry floor 10%, Stabilised scree 9%, Embankment/cutting 8%, Natural cliff face 6%, Hedge 5%.
E (484 records): Stones 51%, Litter 15%, Dead wood 14%, Soil/sand 11%, Human rubbish/garbage 5%.
H (d) Soil/exposed rock (221 records): Calcareous 66%, Non-calcareous 33%.
H (e) Soil (200 records): Loam 57%, Clayey 26%, Sandy 13%.
I (a) Location of animal, horizon (311 records): On ground surface 50%, In litter 22%, Less than 10 cm in soil 20%, More than 10 cm in soil 5%.

T. pygmaeus appears to occur in a wide variety of vegetation and land use types, provided that soil conditions are right. It is a soil-dwelling species which has been recorded in England and Wales mainly on deep, brown earth, calcareous soils, in neutral sandy soils and calcareous clays. In Ireland, it has been recorded frequently in the limestone gravels and sandy soils of the central plain, for example in sandpits and lime-rich grassland and woodland on eskers. It also occurs at coastal sites throughout the British Isles in light free-draining soils, often at the base of sea cliffs. However, it appears to be less frequently recorded on the south coasts of England and Ireland. On the Isle of Wight, where systematic sieving has been employed, it has been found only sparingly.

Records of *T. pygmaeus* made up 10% of all isopod records from depths of more than 10 cm in the soil. It is clearly numerous at some sites; Sutton (unpublished) found it at Wytham Woods, Berkshire, in ungrazed limestone grassland, at densities of 300-600 individuals per m^2. The distribution of records by months shows a bias towards those months when the ground is moist and unfrozen, permitting its discovery near the soil surface, for instance under stones. *T. pygmaeus* shows several distinctive features which probably relate to its soil-dwelling habit, eg the low incidence of gravid females in populations. These features are reviewed by Sutton *et al.* (1984).

Vandel (1960a) considers *T. pygmaeus* to be a soil species which has, by association with man, become widespread throughout most of Europe (except Portugal and the Balkans), North Africa and North America. Its occurrence in Denmark, Norway, Sweden and Finland appears to be mainly associated with glasshouses, nurseries and gardens. *T. pygmaeus* is not particularly associated with synanthropic sites in the British Isles, suggesting that its occurrence here is natural and that it is particularly well adapted to the mild, wet, Atlantic climate of Ireland.

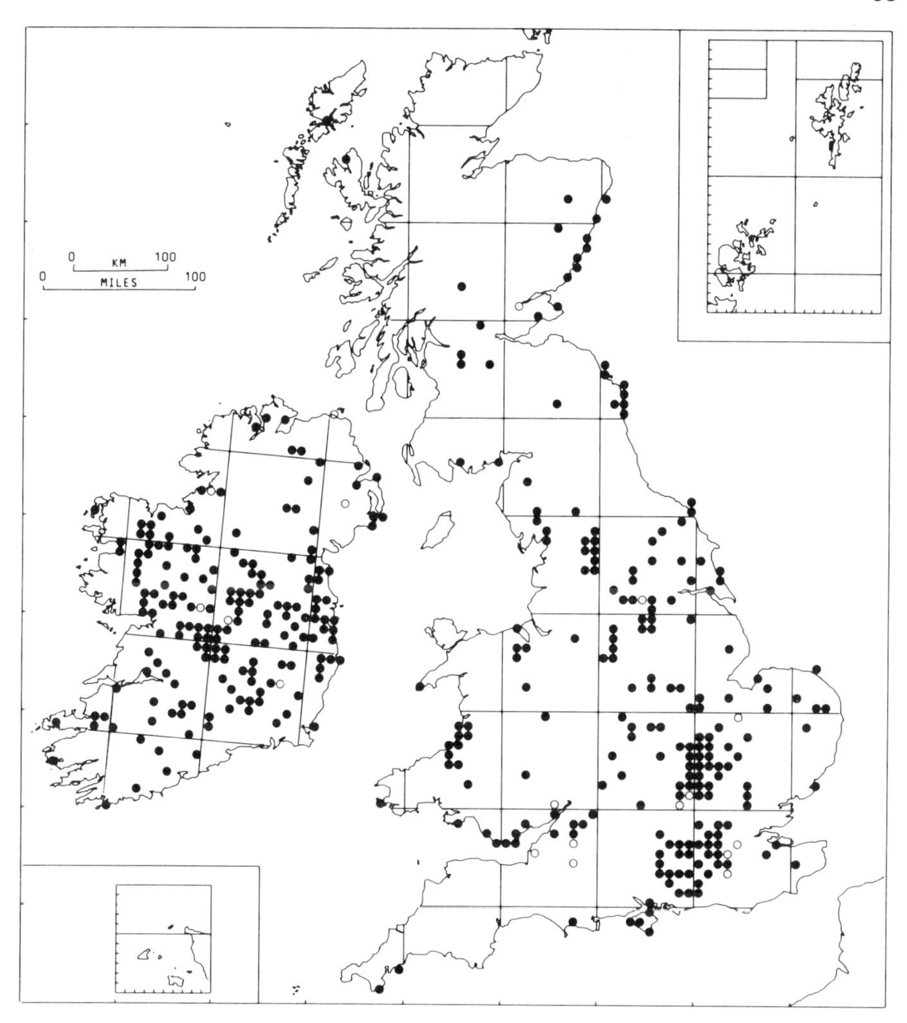

TRICHONISCUS PYGMAEUS

Number of records received: 557

England:	243 records	(44%)
Wales:	47 records	(8%)
Scotland:	27 records	(5%)
Ireland:	240 records	(43%)
Eire:	222 records	(40%)
Northern Ireland:	18 records	(3%)

Number of 10 km squares in which recorded:	430	
Number (%) of records with some habitat data:	484	(87%)
Number (%) of records from 1970 onwards:	520	(93%)

HALOPHILOSCIA COUCHI (Kinahan)

This species is easily confused with pale-coloured juveniles of *Ligia oceanica*. It is almost never seen in the open in daylight, seeking shelter very rapidly when disturbed. It is therefore often difficult to capture, or even to see with any certainty of identification in the field. It grows to about 10 mm in length and is a pale, pinkish, dusty-brown colour.

Halophiloscia couchi was recorded as new to science from Talland Bay, East Cornwall (Kinahan 1858; Bate & Westwood 1868), a site at which it was recorded again in 1976. From recent records, it is known to occur along the southern coast of Britain, from Glamorgan to the Isle of Wight. Its occurrence in Ireland is based on a few records from Howth, Co. Dublin, the most recent being a single specimen found in 1975. The habitat of *H. couchi* at sites on the north coast of Devon and Cornwall was described by Harding (1975). Most records have been from boulder beaches or the bases of sea cliffs in rock-fall debris, also on concrete steps and walls. It has been recorded from several rock types but seems to be more plentiful at sites which are composed of limestone. It is easiest to find at night when the tide is full or rising and has been found in numbers during, or shortly after, rain.

Habitat data

A (35 records): Coastal 100%.
B (35 records): Rural 97%, Suburban/village 3% (at Westward Ho!, North Devon).
C (35 records): Sea 88%, Estuary 4%, Cave threshold 4%, Sparse waste ground 4%.
D (32 records): Shore, etc, 69%, Natural cliff face 16%, Rock & Scree 13%.
E (35 records): Stones 74%, Shingle 11%, Rock 9%.
F (b) Shore (32 records): Splash zone 78%, Intertidal 22%.

The distribution of this species was summarized by Collinge (1942a). He listed 11 localities or areas in Cornwall, Devon (including Lundy Island) and Dorset, and 5 additional sites: near Bognor, West Sussex; Cooden Beach, Kent (in fact, in East Sussex); Canvey Island, South Essex; Walton-on-the-Naze, North Essex, and Banffshire. Material to support these 5 records has not been traced except in the case of Cooden Beach. However, this record, and the possibility that other records from east of the Isle of Wight are correct, suggests that *H. couchi* is probably under-recorded and that it may occur on shingle beaches or other 'soft' coastlines in southern Britain. It is almost certainly under-recorded within its present known range in Britain.

H. couchi occurs on the Atlantic coasts of Europe and north-west Africa and on the coasts of the Mediterranean and the Black Sea, also on the Azores, Madeira, Canaries and Cape Verde Islands. Its occurrence on Howth, Dublin, is particularly notable, being the most northern record for the genus in the world.

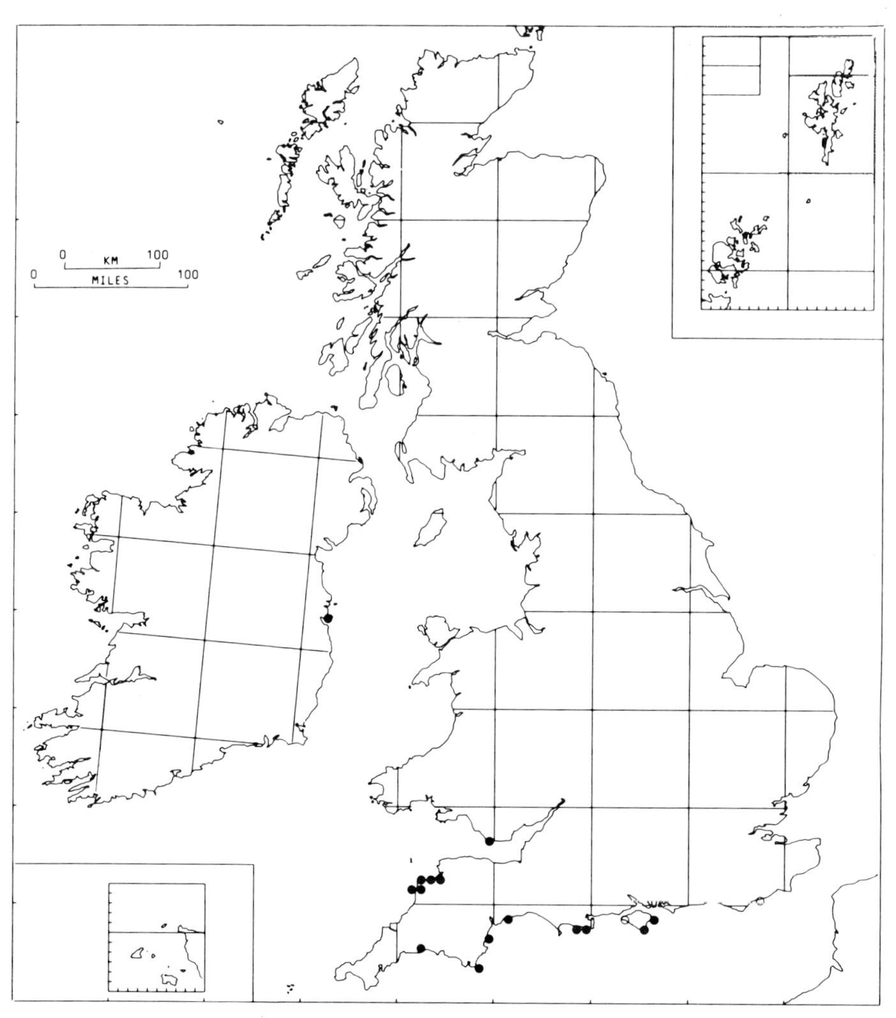

HALOPHILOSCIA COUCHI

Number of records received: 42

England:	37 records	(88%)
Wales:	3 records	(7%)
Ireland:	2 records	(5%)
Eire:	2 records	(5%)

Number of 10 km squares in which recorded:	17	
Number (%) of records with some habitat data:	35	(83%)
Number (%) of records from 1970 onwards:	37	(88%)

[*H. couchi* has been recorded in 1983 and 1984 by A O Chater from several sites on the Cardiganshire coast and at St David's Head, Pembrokeshire.]

STENOPHILOSCIA ZOSTERAE Verhoeff

This species is small (usually less than 6 mm) and elongate, with a distinctly spiny dorsal surface. The colour is white, with only faint brownish mottling on the dorsal surface.

Stenophiloscia zosterae has been found at 3 localities in Britain (Harding, Cotton & Rundle 1980). The first specimens were collected by M J Cotton in March 1974 and February 1976 at Slapton Ley Nature Reserve, South Devon. Subsequently, further specimens were collected by P T Harding at Slapton Ley in June 1977, and a single specimen at Scolt Head Island National Nature Reserve, West Norfolk, in July 1977. A single specimen was collected by A J Rundle at Goldhanger, North Essex, in December 1976.

All the specimens from Slapton Ley and Scolt Head Island were collected in pitfall traps on unvegetated shores composed of shingle and sand. At Scolt Head Island, littoral amphipods were abundant in the traps but they were completely absent from traps at Slapton Ley. The specimen from Goldhanger was collected in daylight in frosty conditions under a stone on a narrow shingle/mud beach below a sea-defence wall on the Blackwater estuary.

Several attempts to find additional material of this species have not been successful: these attempts have included further pitfall trapping on the beaches at Scolt Head Island (September 1977) and Southwold, Suffolk (August 1979), and hand searching by day and night on the beach at Slapton Ley (June 1977) and by day at Goldhanger (November 1977).

On the present evidence, *S. zosterae* is difficult to find and may be rare. However, this apparent rarity could be an artefact and the species may be found to occur at other sites in southern Britain. Some areas which would possibly repay examination are Chesil Beach, Dorset; Dungeness, East Kent; Orfordness, East Suffolk; and the shingle beaches of the west-facing coast of Norfolk.

S. zosterae has been recorded elsewhere only from the Mediterranean coasts of France, Italy, Yugoslavia, Greece and Malta.

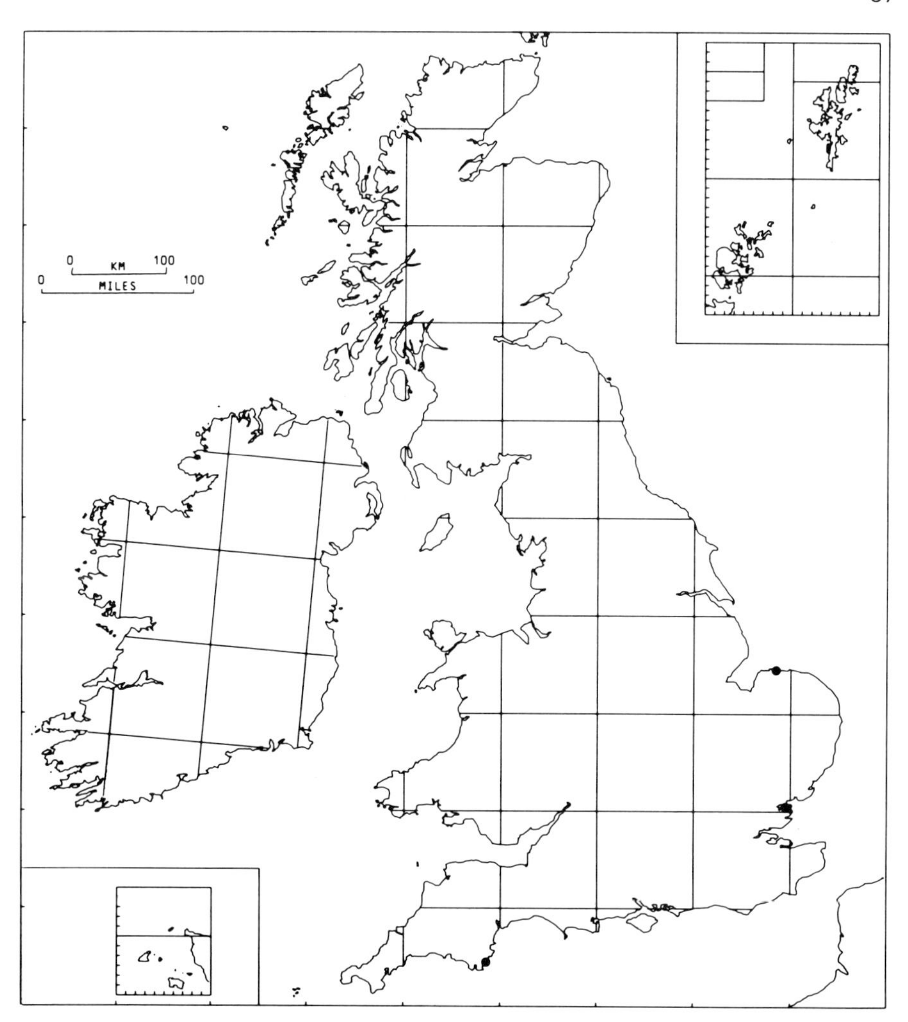

STENOPHILOSCIA ZOSTERAE

Number of records received: 5

England: 5 records

Number of 10 km squares in which recorded: 3
Number of records with some habitat data: 5
Number of records from 1970 onwards: 5

ONISCUS ASELLUS Linnaeus

Oniscus asellus is a large, flat, oval woodlouse with a somewhat shiny appearance. It is mottled grey in colour—except for very occasional colour forms. The young are darker and not shiny, with a characteristic pale patch laterally on the pleon (specifically the epimeron of the 4th pleonite, see Sutton 1972, 1980; Figure 4).

O. asellus is probably our most widely distributed woodlouse, both in terms of its range in the British Isles, and the variety of habitats occupied. It is markedly tolerant of non-calcareous conditions, but does not thrive in dry habitats. The name 'woodlouse' might be said to refer to this species, because it tends to cling tightly to a surface, like a true louse.

It has the distinction of having been recorded in every one of the vice-counties of England, Wales, Scotland and Ireland, and in 72% of the 10 km squares. Of the 27128 records received by the survey, 24% were of *O. asellus*. It is therefore one of the most pervasive of our fauna and flora.

The incidence of coastal records did not increase in the north, and the number of records per vice-county did not diminish, unlike the situation with *Philoscia muscorum* and *Armadillidium vulgare*. This species is well adapted to northern conditions.

Habitat data

A (5614 records): Inland 62%, Coastal 38%.
B (5611 records): Rural 77%, Suburban/village 18%, Urban 5%.
C (5624 records): Waste ground 15%, Woodland, open with herbs/grass 14%, Woodland, other types 13%, Garden 10%, Grassland, lightly grazed 9%, Grassland, ungrazed 8%, Building, outside 6%, Scrubland 5%.
D (2956 records): Roadside verge 22%, Walls 15%, Shore, etc, 9%, Embankment/cutting 7%, Scree 6%, Natural cliff face 6%, Quarry floor 6%, Hedge 6%, Compost/refuse heap 5%. Records from synanthropic sites 65%.
E (5578 records): Stones 42%, Dead wood 25%, Litter 9%, Stone or brickwork 7%, Human rubbish/garbage 5%.
I (a) Location of animal, horizon (3985 records): On ground surface 64%, In litter 15%, Less than 3 m above ground 15%.

O. asellus is a wide-ranging species strongly associated with the underside of stones, dead wood and moist environments. Its penetration of such unpromising woodlouse territory as heather moor owes much to the incidence of rotting fence posts and similar debris. Wherever rotting wood has been lying for some time, there *O. asellus* will surely be. It is notable that it is often the only species to be found in places where there is little lime, as in the blanket bogs of Ireland. A successful colonist of synanthropic situations, it is common in gardens, derelict city areas, parks and glasshouses, and is often very abundant. Curiously, no really thorough work has ever been done on its population biology, and no comprehensive papers have been published.

O. asellus is common throughout most of western and northern Europe, and has spread in association with man to eastern Europe and North America.

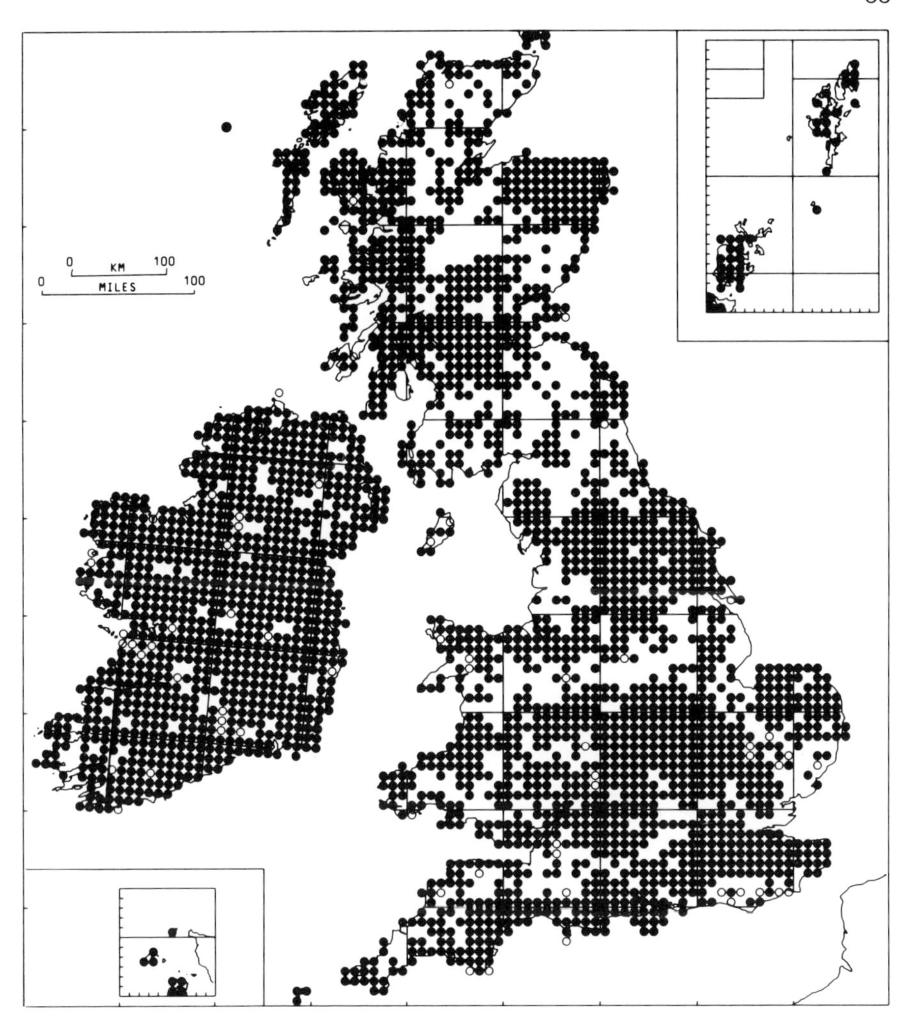

ONISCUS ASELLUS

Number of records received: 6501

England:	3389 records	(52%)	Channel Islands:	28 records	(<1%)
Wales:	445 records	(7%)	Ireland:	1356 records	(21%)
Scotland:	1264 records	(19%)	Eire:	1175 records	(18%)
Isle of Man:	19 records	(<1%)	Northern Ireland:	181 records	(3%)

Number of 10 km squares in which recorded: 2772
Number (%) of records with some habitat data: 5624 (87%)
Number (%) of records from 1970 onwards: 6191 (95%)

PHILOSCIA MUSCORUM (Scopoli)

Philoscia muscorum is the only medium-sized, slim-bodied, long-legged and fast-moving woodlouse which is widespread over the British Isles. It is easily confused in the field with *Ligidium hypnorum*, which is common in woodlands on heavy soils and in marshy places in south-east England, and is also very similar in the field to *Porcellionides cingendus*, which seems partly to replace it in south-west Ireland and cliff sites in south-west England and Wales.

Typically, *P. muscorum* is mottled brown, but attractive yellow/green forms occur on coasts, and a red form occurs at low density in most populations. The species is very common in the south, becoming less so in the north.

Habitat data

A (3341 records): Inland 61%, Coastal 39%.
B (3337 records): Rural 79%, Suburban/village 18%, Urban 3%.
C (3343 records): Grassland, ungrazed 16%, Grassland, lightly grazed 11%, Waste ground, more than 25% vegetation cover 11%, Woodland, open with herbs/grass 9%, Woodland, other 8%, Garden 8%, Grassland, heavily grazed & mown 6%, Scrubland 6%.
D (1757 records): Roadside verge 26%, Shore, etc, 10%, Walls 9%, Embankment/cutting 8%, Hedge 7%, Quarry floor 7%, Natural cliff face 7%. Records from synanthropic sites 66%.
E (3305 records): Stones 35%, Litter 21%, Dead wood 15%, Tussocks 8%, Human rubbish/garbage 5%.
H (a) Litter (1470 records): Mixed grass/herbs 33%, Grass, species unknown 17%, Mixed deciduous 12%, Oak 6%.
I (a) Location of animal, horizon (2275 records): On ground surface 59%, In litter 27%, Less than 3 m above ground 8%, Less than 10 cm in soil 5%.

This species is characteristic of ungrazed calcareous grassland where it may be very abundant. Densities ranging from 240 to 1040 per m^2 were recorded at Spurn Point, South-east Yorkshire, in 1969 and 1970 (Sunderland *et al.* 1976). It also occurs in a very wide range of other habitats. In Scotland, it is confined to coastal areas and very sheltered inland sites, especially in river valleys. Not usually considered to be associated with dead wood, the 15% of records for this microsite is unexpected, except that in grassland the species is often more easily found by hand searching on the underside of fallen fence posts, etc, than in the surrounding turf.

The relationship between *P. muscorum* and *P. cingendus* is interesting. The latter appears to replace *P. muscorum* in south-west Ireland and on the coast in south-west England and Wales, but there is no direct evidence of competition. The same applies to the apparent replacement of *P. muscorum* by *L. hypnorum* on heavy forested soils in south-east England. In Wytham Woods, Berks, *L. hypnorum* occurs on heavy clay, *P. muscorum* on limestone-derived soils. Probably this apparent replacement is the result of their individual tolerances rather than the result of competition. The replacement of *P. muscorum* by *Armadillidium vulgare* as the dominant species at Spurn Point between 1970 and 1976 was associated with changes in the site, due to rabbit grazing, which greatly favoured *A. vulgare* rather than *P. muscorum* (see Davis 1984).

According to Vandel (1960a, 1962), *P. muscorum* is the only '*espèce expansive*' of its genus. It is a dominant species in western Europe and has been widely distributed overseas by man, although it is much less ubiquitous and successful as a colonizer than *Porcellio scaber, Oniscus asellus* and *A. vulgare*.

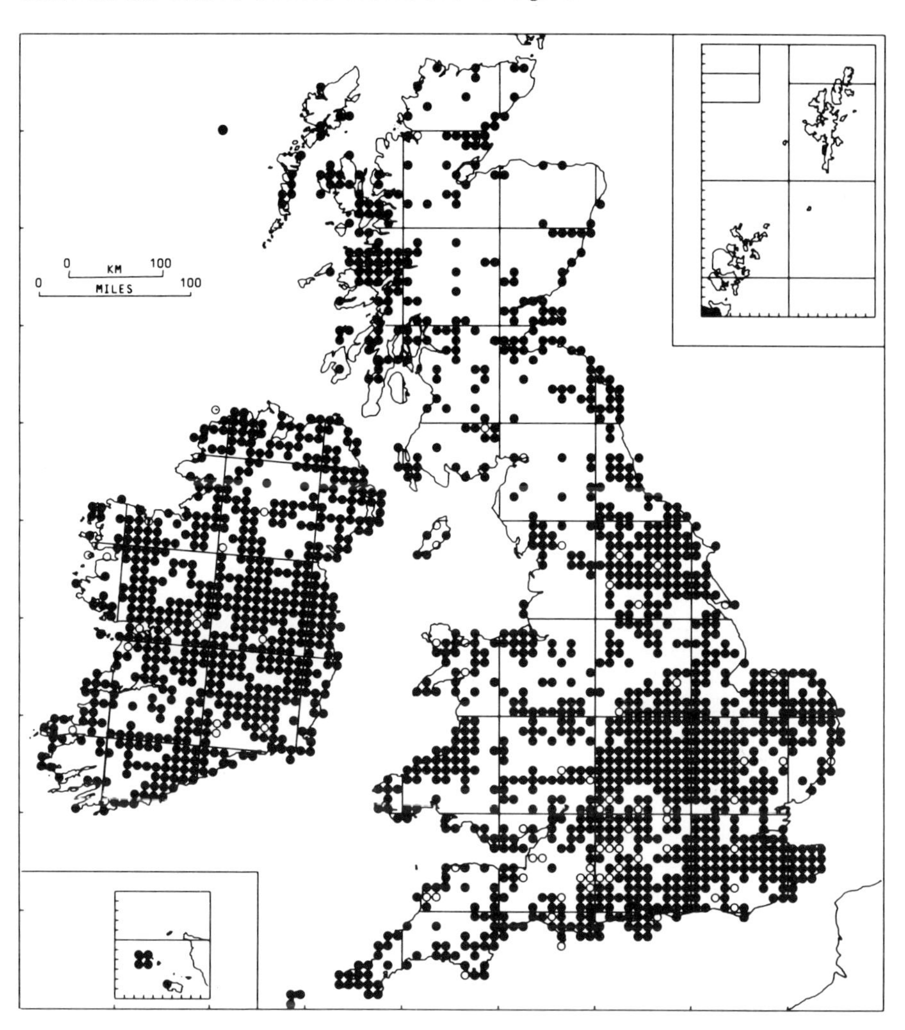

PHILOSCIA MUSCORUM

Number of records received: 3773

England:	2249 records	(60%)	Channel Islands:	12 records	(<1%)
Wales:	234 records	(6%)	Ireland:	918 records	(24%)
Scotland:	349 records	(10%)	Eire:	797 records	(21%)
Isle of Man:	11 records	(<1%)	Northern Ireland:	121 records	(3%)

Number of 10 km squares in which recorded: 1823
Number (%) of records with some habitat data: 3343 (88%)
Number (%) of records from 1970 onwards: 3369 (89%)

PLATYARTHRUS HOFFMANNSEGGI Brandt

Platyarthrus hoffmannseggi is a small, eyeless, white woodlouse with a distinctive oval outline and short, stout antennae. In Britain, it is found most often in ants' nests, and it is by far the most common isopod associated with ants, comprising 59% of all records from this microsite. It is also commonly found under flat stones, usually associated with ants, but not necessarily in nests. It is frequently found in the nests of *Lasius flavus, L. niger* and *Myrmica* species, but has been recorded in association with other species in the British Isles and Europe (Donisthorpe 1927).

Habitat data

A (453 records): Inland 60%, Coastal 40%.
B (452 records): Rural 72%, Suburban/village 23%, Urban 5%.
C (452 records): Grassland, ungrazed & lightly grazed 26%, Waste ground 20%, Garden 19%, Grassland, heavily grazed & mown 9%, Woodland 6%.
D (241 records): Roadside verge 18%, Embankment/cutting 13%, Walls 12%, Quarry floor 9%, Natural cliff face 7%, Flower bed 7%, Shore, etc, 6%, Screes 5%.
E (451 records): Ant nests 54%, Stones 24%.
H (d) Soil/exposed rock (185 records): Calcareous 84%, Non-calcareous 16%.
H (e) Soil (194 records): Loam 37%, Clayey 28%, Sandy 28%.
I (a) Location of animal, horizon (317 records): On ground surface 54%, Less than 10 cm in soil 34%.

The nature of the relationship between *P. hoffmannseggi* and the ants with which it lives has never been fully investigated, but it is thought that the main source of food for the isopod is the ants' faeces. Brooks (1942) demonstrated that *P. hoffmannseggi* is attracted towards formic acid vapour. The species seems well suited to life amongst ants, with behavioural reactions which include the discharge of a defensive secretion (Gorvett & Taylor 1960) and the ability to hold itself tight against a substrate when disturbed. Morphologically, its oval outline gives little purchase for a predator wishing to prise it away from the substrate.

The distribution of *P. hoffmannseggi* is largely related to the distributions of the ants with which it is found. The south-easterly bias in the distribution in Britain is reflected by the distribution of, for example, *Lasius* spp. (Barrett 1979) and, like *Lasius* spp., *P. hoffmannseggi* seems to be restricted to coastal sites in the north. The most northerly site is near Inverkeithing, Fifeshire, where it was found by Evans (1900) and it has subsequently been rediscovered associated with *Formica lemani* and *Myrmica rubra*. At Warton Crag, West Lancashire, it occurs with *Myrmica ruginodis* in limestone grassland. In Ireland, it is typically found in undisturbed lime-rich grassland, on open, southerly, free-draining slopes, often where the soil is slightly sandy and where grazing pressure is slight.

P. hoffmannseggi is widespread throughout much of western, central and eastern Europe, from the Mediterranean north to the Netherlands, Denmark and southern Sweden. The British Isles are the north-western limit of its natural distribution.

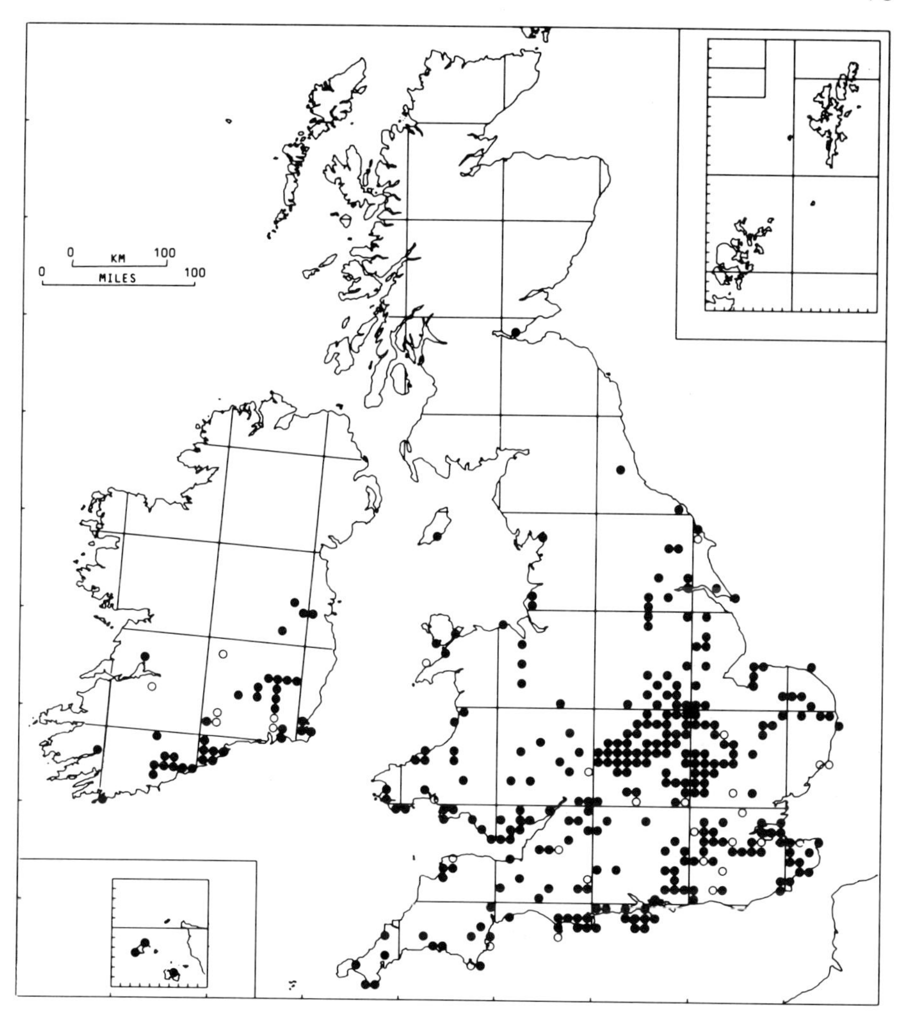

PLATYARTHRUS HOFFMANNSEGGI

Number of records received: 542

England:	412 records	(76%)
Wales:	63 records	(11%)
Scotland:	3 records	(<1%)
Isle of Man:	1 record	(<1%)
Channel Islands:	3 records	(<1%)
Ireland:	60 records	(11%)
Eire:	60 records	(11%)

Number of 10 km squares in which recorded:	347	
Number (%) of records with some habitat data:	452	(83%)
Number (%) of records from 1970 onwards:	470	(87%)

ARMADILLIDIUM ALBUM Dollfus

This is a distinctive species in several ways. Its colour varies little: a background of off-white or pale straw, flecked with grey or light brown, resembling the sand with which it is usually associated. The dorsal surface is minutely spiny and the eyes are distinctly black. It has only been recorded from coastal sites: rarely active in daylight, it usually remains immobile if exposed, in a slightly arched position with one or 2 pairs of legs protruding at either side.

First recorded from the British Isles in 1906 or 1907, at the estuary of the Taw and Torridge, North Devon (Cummings 1907), *A. album* was next recorded in 1961 on Whiteford Sands, Glamorgan (Cotton 1967). Surveys of dune systems, mainly in western Britain and eastern Ireland, recorded this species at several sites (Harding 1968a, 1969) and additional sites have been added recently. Some sites have not been re-surveyed since 1970.

Habitat data

A (44 records): Coastal 100%.
B (44 records): Rural 100%
C (44 records): Sand dunes 82%, Salt marsh 14%, Sea & Estuary 4%.
D (38 records): Shore, etc, 100%.
E (44 records): Shoreline jetsam 75%, Dead wood 23%, Human rubbish/garbage 2%.
F (b) (27 records): Splash zone 56%, Between splash zone and 100 m 44%.
H (e) (36 records): Pure sand 86%, Sandy 14%.

On dune systems, it usually occurs in the upper drift lines of sandy beaches, particularly under drift material in the fore-dunes (where *Cakile maritima, Salsola kali* and *Elymus farctus* grow). Similarly, in salt marshes it occurs in the upper drift zones, above the limits of normal high tides. Found under drift wood, clinging to it or secreted in crevices, it is normally found in small numbers—rarely singly. It is able to burrow into sand and has been found up to 10 cm deep under drift material. Observations at Scolt Head Island, West Norfolk, have shown it to be active at night on the surface in salt marsh jetsam and on the nearby beach. It has often been recorded with amphipods, but rarely where the latter are abundant, and also occasionally with other woodlice *(Porcellio scaber, Armadillidium vulgare* and *Eluma purpurascens).*

Many potential sites on large dune systems and estuaries have been examined unsuccessfully for this species. Some were clearly disturbed by man (eg Studland, Dorset), or were scoured by strong tides and winds (eg many Scottish sites). Others were less obviously unsuitable, eg on the south coasts of Wexford and Waterford, and in western Ireland, but many had much coarser sand than typical *A. album* sites.

Several localities where *A. album* has been recorded in Britain are nature reserves or Sites of Special Scientific Interest. Disturbance by man appears to reduce the numbers of this species at some sites around the Bristol Channel, and at least one Irish site is being excavated for sand; also supralittoral species, such as this, are vulnerable to marine pollution as at Spurn Head, South-east Yorkshire. *A. album* is sufficiently uncommon to warrant concern about its future at some sites. It has been recorded from the Madeira Islands, Italy, France, and the Netherlands. The site on Luce Bay, Wigtownshire, is the northernmost so far recorded.

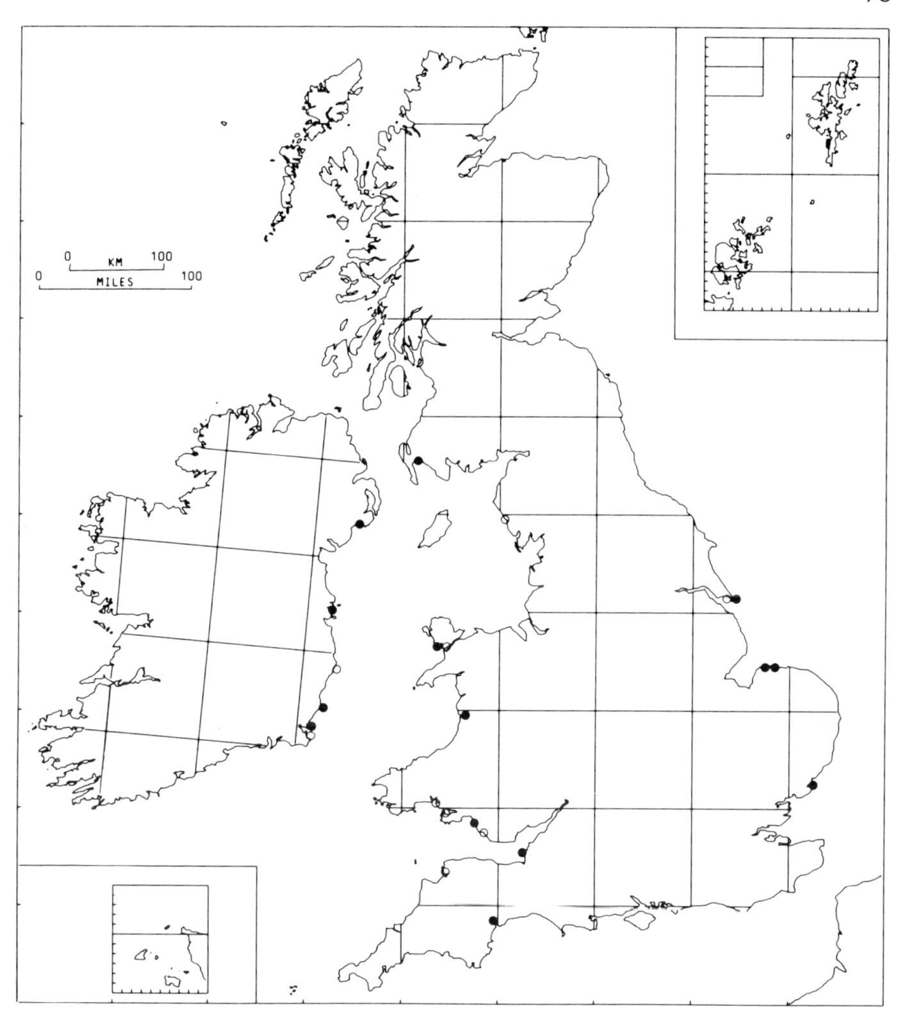

ARMADILLIDIUM ALBUM

Number of records received: 45

England:	17 records	(38%)
Wales:	12 records	(27%)
Scotland:	1 record	(2%)
Ireland:	15 records	(33%)
Eire:	14 records	(31%)
Northern Ireland:	1 record	(2%)

Number of 10 km squares in which recorded:	23	
Number (%) of records with some habitat data:	44	(98%)
Number (%) of records from 1970 onwards:	23	(51%)

ARMADILLIDIUM DEPRESSUM Brandt

Armadillidium depressum is a large, stout pill woodlouse, up to 20 mm in length. Males are slate-grey in colour and females exhibit various degrees of yellowish mottling in longitudinal stripes. An inability to roll up into a perfect sphere (the telson and the antennae remain protruding) is the most obvious field character distinguishing this species (and *Armadillidium nasatum*) from the commoner *Armadillidium vulgare*. Upon closer inspection, it will be seen that the scutellum is larger and broader than that of *A. vulgare* and protrudes above the top of the head; in *A. nasatum*, the scutellum is narrow and more strongly protruding. The whole animal is broad and the margins of the epimera curve outwards (like the back of a tortoise shell); in *A. vulgare*, the epimera margins terminate vertically, giving a hemispherical outline when seen from behind.

Habitat data

A (100 records): Coastal 61%, Inland 39%.
B (100 records): Suburban/village 43%, Rural 33%, Urban 24%.
C (100 records): Garden 34%, Waste ground 25%, Building 16%, Grassland, ungrazed and lightly grazed 12%. Records from synanthropic sites 50%.
D (69 records): Wall with mortar 30%, Quarry floor 13%, Rockery 9%, Compost/refuse heap 6%, Natural cliff face 6%, Road/path 5%. Records from synanthropic sites 81%.
E (100 records): Stones 48%, Stone or brickwork 25%, Rock 9%, Human rubbish/garbage 5%.
H (d) Soil/exposed rock (51 records): Calcareous 86%, Non-calcareous 14%.
(e) Soil (28 records): Loam 71%, Clayey 18%.
I (a) Location of animal, horizon (75 records): On ground surface 63%, Less than 3 m above ground 20%.

This species has an essentially south-western distribution in Britain, occurring in Devon, Dorset and either side of the Severn estuary. There are also coastal records from Pembrokeshire and Cardiganshire. All the outlying records are from synanthropic sites: a mortared wall at Llanybydder, Cardiganshire; a heated glasshouse near Cheltenham, East Gloucestershire; a church wall at Shipton-under-Wychwood, Oxfordshire; a railway bridge near Quainton, Buckinghamshire; and scree beds at Kew Gardens, Surrey.

It sometimes occurs in very large numbers (eg in gardens at Ilfracombe, North Devon), and may be found together with either or both *A. vulgare* and *A. nasatum*, especially in synanthropic locations. It will enter and inhabit buildings, especially cellars, damp halls and kitchens. *A. depressum*, like *A. vulgare*, can dig very well and will produce a network of burrows where it can survive extremes of temperature, and dry periods. Its distribution, centred in the south-west, is unique among British woodlice, and would make an interesting subject for further study.

According to Vandel (1962), *Armadillidium depressum* occurs only in Britain, France and Italy.

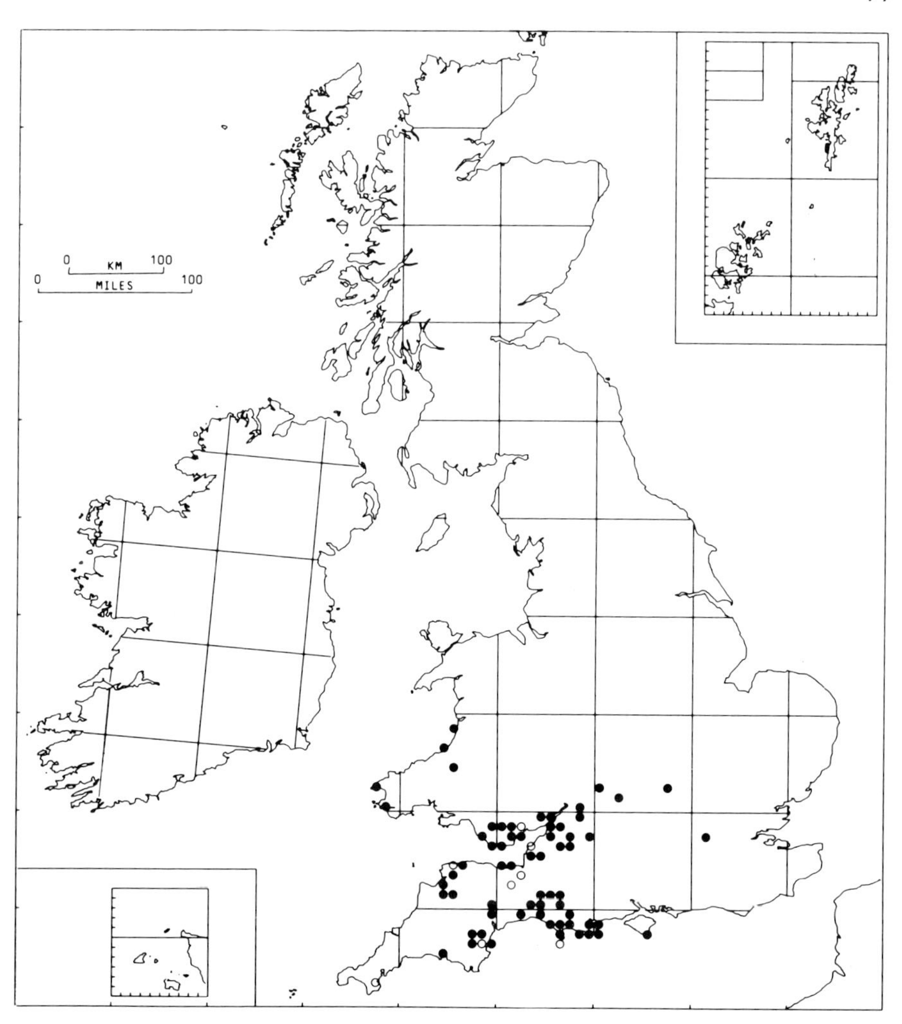

ARMADILLIDIUM DEPRESSUM

Number of records received: 121

England:	99 records	(82%)
Wales:	22 records	(18%)

Number of 10 km squares in which recorded:	71	
Number (%) of records with some habitat data:	100	(83%)
Number (%) of records from 1970 onwards:	105	(87%)

ARMADILLIDIUM NASATUM Budde-Lund

Both sexes are generally brownish-grey in colour with longitudinal bands of pale and dark mottling, but brick-red and yellowish individuals have been found. Like *Armadillidium depressum*, the first field character to distinguish *Armadillidium nasatum* from *Armadillidium vulgare* (with which it may be found) is its inability to roll up into a perfect ball: the antennae and the telson remain protruding from the sphere. The scutellum of *A. nasatum* is produced into a distinct 'nose', a square projection, clearly visible with the naked eye, between the antennae on the front of the head. This feature immediately distinguishes *A. nasatum* from all the other species of *Armadillidium*. The telson is relatively longer and more rounded than that of related species and the whole body of *A. nasatum* is slimmer than the other large species.

Habitat data

A (113 records): Coastal 52%, Inland 48%.
B (113 records): Rural 70%, Suburban/village 22%, Urban 8%.
C (112 records): Grassland 26%, Waste ground 18%, Building 13%, Woodland 12%, Coastal—Estuary, Sea, Sand dune 11%, Garden 8%. Records from synanthropic sites 25%.
D (67 records): Quarries 22%, Shore, etc, 15%, Screes 13%, Roadside verge 10%, Embankment/cutting 7%. Records from synanthropic sites 58%.
E (111 records): Stones 47%, Stone or brickwork 9%, Rock 6%, Soil/sand 6%, Litter 6%, Dead wood 6%.
H (d) Soil/exposed rock (70 records): Calcareous 81%, Non-calcareous 19%.

A. nasatum has been recorded at several sites, mainly in south-west England, as an apparently natural constituent of the calcareous or coastal grassland fauna, eg Rodborough Common, West Gloucestershire, and The Lizard, West Cornwall. Elsewhere it appears to thrive locally in areas of disturbed grassland where insolation is high, eg disused quarry sites, especially in Surrey and Kent, and railway embankments, eg in Warwickshire. More recently the survey has revealed that this species occurs in garden centres, either in association with Oolitic limestone for rockeries (Harding 1982) or in glasshouses (A J Rundle, pers. comm.). It has also been recorded from a stonemason's yard at Aylsham, East Norfolk. The association of this species with quarries was emphasized (using data provided by the survey) by Davis and Jones (1978) and its association with glasshouses has been known for many years. It was recognized as a common glasshouse pest, especially in the Lee Valley, Hertfordshire, but many of these records were made under the name *Armadillidium speyeri* Jackson. It has also been recorded as a pest in a block of flats near Torquay, South Devon, living mainly in cavity walls.

This species has expanded its distribution by association with man and with man-made habitats. From the centre of its distribution in northern Italy (Vandel 1962), it has been recorded in the open from France, northern Spain and Limburg (Netherlands) and elsewhere in Europe, mainly in glasshouses, horticultural nurseries and botanic gardens. According to Schultz (1961), it was first recorded in North America in 1902 and is now widespread, mainly on the eastern seaboard, and naturalized in some locations.

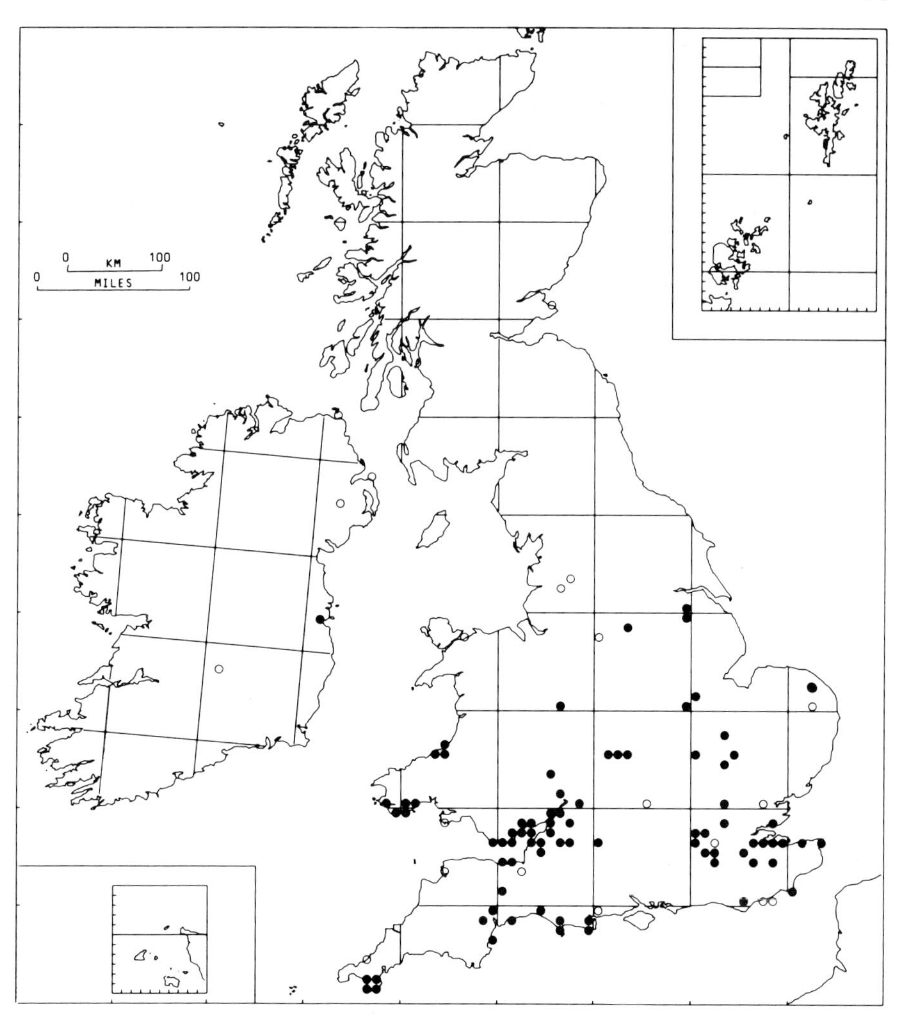

ARMADILLIDIUM NASATUM

Number of records received: 158

England:	117 records	(74%)
Wales:	33 records	(21%)
Scotland:	1 record	(<1%)
Ireland:	7 records	(5%)
Eire:	4 records	(3%)
Northern Ireland:	3 records	(2%)

Number of 10 km squares in which recorded:	101	
Number (%) of records with some habitat data:	113	(72%)
Number (%) of records from 1970 onwards:	123	(78%)

ARMADILLIDIUM PICTUM Brandt

The colour of *Armadillidium pictum* is similar to that of *Armadillidium pulchellum* but is somewhat darker and with less distinctive mottling, arranged in longitudinal lines. The epimera, particularly those of the pereon, are frequently pale-coloured. The colour tends to fade in alcohol to give an appearance similar to that of the pale grey forms of *Armadillidium vulgare. A. pictum* when full grown reaches 7–9 mm in length and is therefore larger than *A. pulchellum*.

Probably because of its similarity to *A. pulchellum* and *A. vulgare, A. pictum* seems to have been the victim of repeated mis-identification. Many early records of *A. pictum* have proved to be of the other 2 species. Specimens to support the original records from limestone sites around Morecambe Bay (Standen 1913) have not been traced, but these records are probably reliable in view of its recent occurrence in this area. Collinge (1944c) listed 17 localities in 11 counties in England and Wales; 3 of these localities have been confirmed by subsequent records and one by examination of voucher specimens, but a further 5 localities have been shown by Harding (1977) to be based on mis-identification. The remaining 8 localities have not been substantiated. Subsequent records for Cambridgeshire (Ing 1959) and Kirkcudbrightshire (Crowson & Crowson 1963) have proved to be mis-identifications.

The one early record confirmed by the examination of preserved material was from 'Catrick Force, Ribblehead', collected by F Rhodes in 1917. This location is almost certainly Catrigg Force near Stainforth, in Ribblesdale, Mid-west Yorkshire.

More recent valid records have been from 5 localities in Westmorland and West Lancaster, and one in Breconshire. All these records were from rocky terrain (rock pavement, scree, dry stone wall) within woodland or scrub or adjacent to woodland.

The rocks at the sites varied considerably: in the Morecambe Bay area at Gait Barrows, Arnside and Silverdale, Carboniferous limestone; and in the Lake District at Brantwood, Silurian strata and at Hartsop, Borrowdale volcanic series. At Tarren yr Esgob, Breconshire, it occurred on tufa screes from Old Red Sandstone. Specimens were most commonly found during daylight under stones and among moss. At Gait Barrows, one specimen was beaten from the lower branches of a juniper bush. Experience at Tarren yr Esgob suggests that it is capable of burrowing to considerable depths, supporting the observation of Vandel (1962) that it can be collected at depths of one or 2 metres in the soil of dry woods.

As all 6 British sites are remote and isolated from human habitations, it seems probable that *A. pictum* is part of the native fauna.

In Europe, it is considered to be a forest species (Meinertz 1950; Vandel 1962), occurring in France, Switzerland, Germany, the Benelux countries, Denmark and southern Scandinavia.

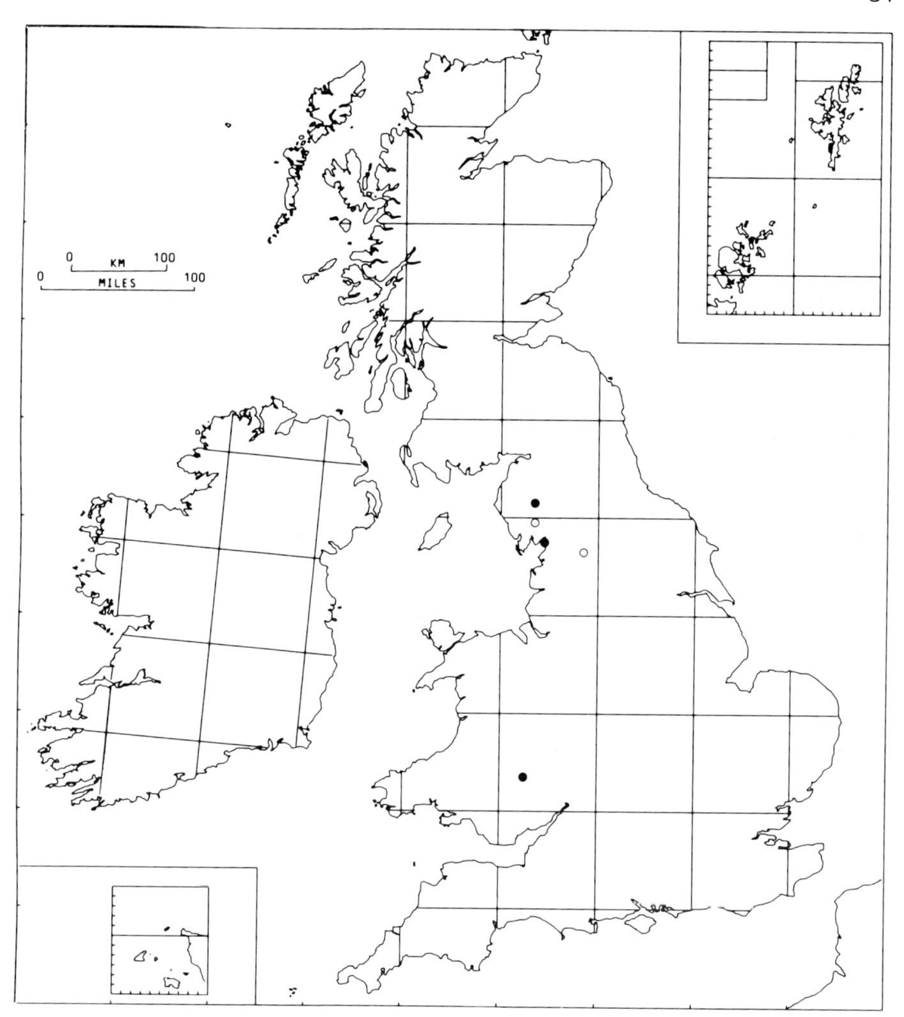

ARMADILLIDIUM PICTUM

Number of records received: 8

England:	6 records
Wales:	2 records

Number of 10 km squares in which recorded:	5
Number of records with some habitat data:	7
Number of records from 1970 onwards:	5

ARMADILLIDIUM PULCHELLUM (Zencker)

This small (5–6 mm) pill woodlouse is attractively and distinctively marked. The first impression is of a dark brown species with ginger-orange patches, in fact made up of a mosaic of black, orange, white and red. Usually there are parallel rows of light flecks running along either side of the dorso-median line, and a noticeably darker patch on the outer edges of the last segment of the pleon. This latter feature preserves well in alcohol, whereas the paler colour fades, and it is useful for rapidly distinguishing *Armadillidium pulchellum* from well-marked forms of *Armadillidium vulgare. Armadillidium pictum* also has a mottled appearance but is larger (7–9 mm) and has less distinctive colouration. The seventh segment of the pleon, although darkly mottled in *A. pictum*, is also less striking.

Habitat data

A (71 records): Coastal 51%, Inland 49%.
B (71 records): Rural 100%.
C (71 records): Grassland, lightly grazed 26%, Grassland, ungrazed 18%, Grassland, heavily grazed 13%, Scrubland, open with herbs/grass 11%, Acid heath/moor, mixed 10%.
D (52 records): Stabilised scree 48%, Natural cliff face 23%, Unstabilised scree 10%, Rock pavement 6%.
E (71 records): Stones 63%, Litter 14%, Rock 6%.
H (d) Soil/exposed rock (62 records): Calcareous 68%, Non-calcareous 32%.

Some of the situations from which *A. pulchellum* has been recorded in Britain differ from those in Ireland. Most British records have been from inland districts on Carboniferous limestone in Derbyshire, Yorkshire, north Wales and the Lake District, or from coastal cliffs and cliff tops on various Paleozoic rocks. A few Irish coastal sites are known and it has been recorded from limestone outcrops in the Burren, Clare and Lough Dargan, Sligo, but most of the recent Irish records have been from dry calcareous glacial sands, often formed into eskers, in the midlands. At such sites in Ireland, *A. pulchellum* has occurred in association with mats of *Thymus praecox, Carlina vulgaris* and ant hills, in ungrazed or lightly grazed grassland. At almost all these inland sites in Ireland, *A. pulchellum* was confined to areas of only a few square metres. Almost all British records have been from under stones or under mats of *Thymus* spp., mosses or *Sedum anglicum* growing over stones, especially on screes. Although the microsites were usually damp, the surrounding grassland or rocky terrain was often dry on the surface. No sites have been recorded in Britain which are similar to those on glacial sands found in midland Ireland.

A. pulchellum and *A. vulgare* are known to occur together at only one site in the British Isles, at Arnside Knott, Westmorland. This site is on Carboniferous limestone, facing south, about 1.5 km from the coast and 140 m above sea level. The grassland is in places quite long, possibly favouring *A. vulgare*, with *A. pulchellum* mainly in shorter turf associated with *Lasius* and other ants. The populations at this site are probably too small to survive intensive sampling over a period of time to examine the interaction of the 2 species.

The British Isles probably contain the greatest concentration of known sites for this species. It appears to be limited to north-western Europe, including southern Scandinavia.

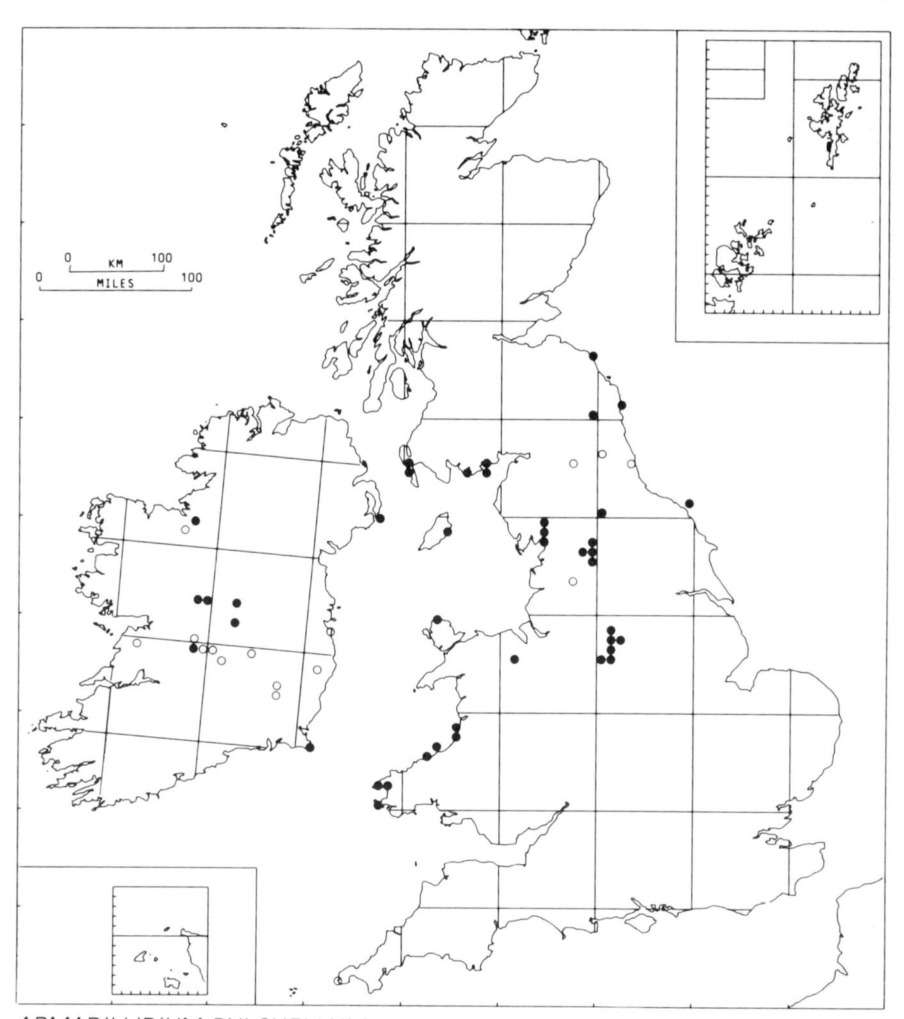

ARMADILLIDIUM PULCHELLUM

Number of records received: 98

England:	45 records	(46%)
Wales:	18 records	(18%)
Scotland:	10 records	(10%)
Isle of Man:	2 records	(2%)
Ireland:	23 records	(24%)
Eire:	21 records	(22%)
Northern Ireland:	2 records	(2%)

Number of 10 km squares in which recorded:	57	
Number (%) of records with some habitat data:	72	(73%)
Number (%) of records from 1970 onwards:	77	(78%)

ARMADILLIDIUM VULGARE (Latreille)

This is the only pill woodlouse which is widespread or common in any part of the British Isles. *Armadillidium depressum* is occasionally as common, at a few sites in south-west England and south Wales. *Armadillidium vulgare* is variable in colour, from the most usual, slate grey, through shades of brown and red, to occasional specimens which are pale and mottled, not unlike *Armadillidium album*.

Habitat data

A (1810 records): Inland 59%, Coastal 41%.
B (1804 records): Rural 74%, Suburban/village 21%, Urban 5%.
C (1813 records): Waste ground 22%, Grassland, ungrazed 16%, Grassland, other 13%, Garden 11%, Woodland 7%, Buildings 5%, Sand dunes 5%, Arable 5%.
D (1073 records): Roadside verge 23%, Natural cliff face 10%, Quarry floor 9%, Shore, etc, 9%, Embankment/cutting 7%, Wall with mortar 7%, Compost/refuse heap 6%. Records from synanthropic sites 69%.
E (1793 records): Stones 38%, Litter 12%, Dead wood 11%, Human rubbish/garbage 7%, Tussocks 7%, Stone or brickwork 7%.
H (d) Soil/exposed rock (651 records): Calcareous 80%, Non-calcareous 20%.
I (a) Location of animal, horizon (1228 records): On ground surface 65%, Litter 17%, Less than 10 cm in soil 9%.

Although common and widespread in the south and east of Britain and Ireland, its occurrence becomes increasingly coastal or synanthropic in the north and west. It has not been recorded further north than a line from the Clyde to the Tay in Scotland, or further north-west than a line from Galway city to Lough Foyle in Ireland. It is possible that isolated populations exist beyond these limits, for instance in glasshouses. Almost all the inland records in Scotland were from gardens or glasshouses—a notable exception being Salisbury Crags, Edinburgh (Harding, Collis & Collis 1979).

Many of the extremities of its occurrence are on sand dunes and other coastal sites (eg Isle of Whithorn, Wigtownshire, and Magilligan, Londonderry). In the south and west, the species is often abundant on coastal cliffs, and inland from cliffs, where sea spray derivatives apparently compensate for the acid nature of the substrate.

In southern areas it is often plentiful in gardens and, as the above figures suggest, in calcareous grassland. It appears to be absent from areas of upland Carboniferous limestone grassland, eg in Derbyshire, the Craven area of Yorkshire and in the Burren, Clare. In these areas the much smaller *Armadillidium pulchellum* occurs. Some apparently suitable sites in the north and west have been searched but *A. vulgare* has not been found (eg the limestone of Durness, West Sutherland, and Belmullet, West Mayo).

A. vulgare is probably the woodlouse which is most familiar to casual observers in the south of the British Isles. It is often seen in the open in full daylight and can withstand dry conditions, but is not usually seen in the open in windy weather when water loss is more rapid. *A. vulgare* has been the subject of several detailed studies: of genetics (Howard 1981) and of population dynamics (Paris 1963; Lawlor 1976b; Davis 1984).

It has been recorded throughout Europe, except in the higher latitudes and altitudes, and parts of Asia. It seems to have been spread by man to many other continents including North America, Australasia, South Africa and some Pacific and Atlantic islands.

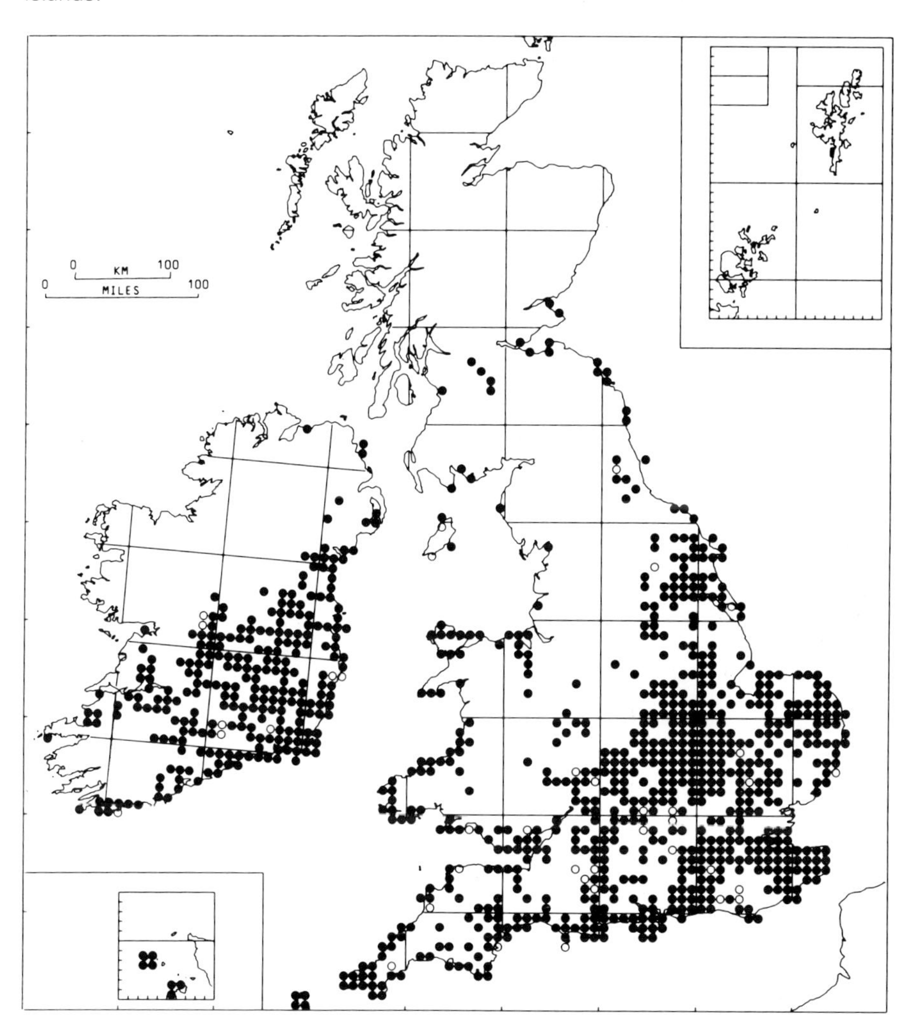

ARMADILLIDIUM VULGARE

Number of records received: 2116

England:	1488 records	(70%)	Channel Islands:	12 records	(<1%)
Wales:	178 records	(8%)	Ireland:	407 records	(19%)
Scotland:	26 records	(1%)	Eire:	395 records	(19%)
Isle of Man:	5 records	(<1%)	Northern Ireland:	12 records	(<1%)

Number of 10 km squares in which recorded: 955
Number (%) of records with some habitat data: 1813 (86%)
Number (%) of records from 1970 onwards: 1885 (89%)

ELUMA PURPURASCENS Budde-Lund

This pill woodlouse occasionally reaches about 15 mm in length but, generally, specimens average about 10 mm. The body colour is usually purplish-brown but the most distinctive features are the eyes, which are composed of single large black ocelli, and the telson, which is triangular.

Eluma purpurascens was first discovered in the British Isles on the southern cliffs of Howth, Dublin, in August 1908 (Pack Beresford 1908), a site at which it is still abundant. Since then it has been found to be common along the coast of Dublin from North Bull Island to the Portrane peninsula; further north in the county it has been found only at Rush and Skerries. Despite careful searching of apparently suitable sites on the coast north of Skerries, it has not been recorded; and it has not been found on the 2 islands off the coast of Dublin, Ireland's Eye and Lambay Island. It is known to occur at one coastal site south of Dublin at Newcastle, Wicklow, and at 2 inland sites in Kildare.

This species was not recorded in Britain until 1975 when it was found at Overstrand, East Norfolk (Harding 1976b). Since then, it has been found at Hampton near Herne Bay, East Kent, in 1980 and was re-found at Overstrand in 1981. Both sites are rather unstable 'soft rock' coastal cliffs: of glacial deposits at Overstrand and of brick-earth at Hampton. This type of coastal cliff is not common.

Habitat data

A (36 records): Coastal 94%, Inland 6%.
B (35 records): Rural 71%, Suburban/village 29%.
C (36 records): Grassland 33%, Waste ground 31%, Sand dunes 17%.
D (26 records): Natural cliff face 50%, Shore, etc, 27%.
E (35 records): Litter 31%, Stones 26%, Tussocks 11%, Soil/sand 9%, Dead wood 9%.

Although this species appears to be very closely tied to coastal locations in Ireland and Britain, particularly vegetated coastal cliffs, it is not dependent on coastal conditions. The 2 inland sites in Kildare are associated with railway lines, as is the coastal site in Wicklow. Its absence from similar areas on these and other railway lines in eastern Ireland suggests that it may not have reached the sites by gradual dispersal but may instead have been introduced with railway ballast. The ballast used almost certainly originated from a limestone quarry at Feltrim Hill, a site 2½ km inland from the coast of Dublin, at which *E. purpurascens* has been recorded.

The status of this species in the British Isles is uncertain. Vandel (1962) considered that *E. purpurascens* occurs naturally in upland areas of Portugal, Spain and North Africa. In these areas it occupies forests or, as a relic after forest clearance, caves. He considered that its occurrence in Ireland and western France and on various Atlantic islands was a result of introduction by man.

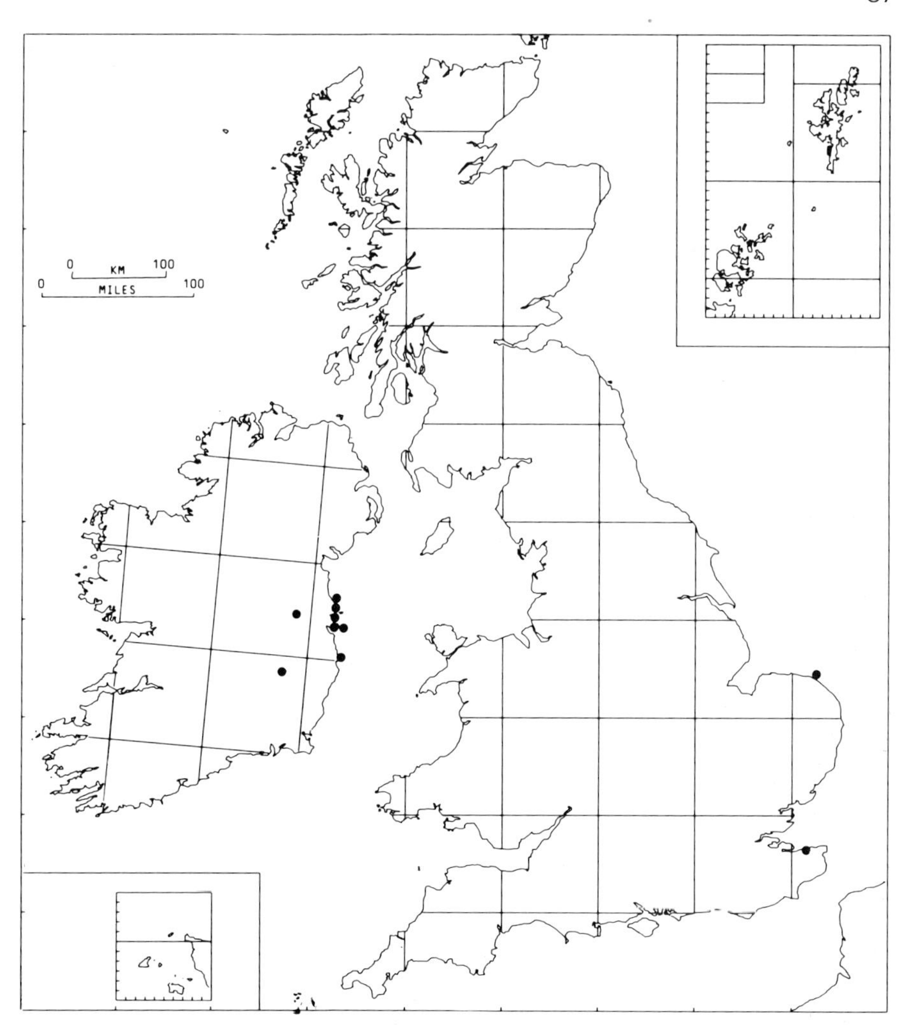

ELUMA PURPURASCENS

Number of records received: 37

England:	8 records	(22%)
Ireland:	29 records	(78%)
Eire:	29 records	(78%)

Number of 10 km squares in which recorded:	10	
Number (%) of records with some habitat data:	36	(97%)
Number (%) of records from 1970 onwards:	36	(97%)

CYLISTICUS CONVEXUS (De Geer)

This is a distinctive species, recognizable in the field by its colouration and shape. It is a pale, occasionally brownish, grey; the pereonites each have a translucent patch either side of the midline and a pale flash on the edges of the epimera. The bases of the uropods are typically buff, yellow or pale orange and contrast distinctively with the greyish telson. The body is highly arched, similar to *Armadillidium* spp. The animal is able to roll into an open ball, but seldom does so without provocation. Unlike *Armadillidium* spp., *Cylisticus convexus* has cylindrical uropods, which stick out when the animal is rolled up.

Habitat data

A (119 records): Coastal 55%, Inland 45%.
B (119 records): Rural 44%, Suburban/village 34%, Urban 22%.
C (119 records): Waste ground 36%, Sea & Estuary 23%, Garden 13%, Building 13%, Grassland (all types) 6%.
D (74 records): Shore, etc, 20%, Roadside verge 14%, Screes 12%, Wall with mortar 11%, Natural cliff face 9%, Flower bed 8%, Quarry floor 8%.
E (117 records): Stones 45%, Stone or brickwork 15%, Dead wood 9%, Human rubbish/garbage 5%.

There are indications of 2 elements in the distribution: natural coastal sites, and synanthropic sites. Of the 1st Order Habitats, 23% of records are from *Sea, Estuary* and *Salt marsh*, and 62% of records can be considered to be synanthropic. The 2nd Order Habitats bring out the importance of *Shore, etc*, but also *Screes* and *Cliffs* as natural habitats.

The natural habitats share common features such as exposure, lack of vegetation cover and disturbance. The ability of *C. convexus* to exist in these habitats may account for its apparent success at invading synanthropic sites such as quarries, walls and waste ground, for these areas show features similar to the natural sites. Vandel (1962) reported a similar range of habitats throughout Europe and Asia Minor. He described *C. convexus* as being xerophilic with a preference for exposed sunny positions, but reported that this species is most frequently found in association with man. This synanthropic nature may account for its introduction into North Africa, Canada, USA, Mexico and Argentina. In the British Isles, there is little evidence of this species occurring in caves and mines, as described for France by Vandel.

The expected distribution pattern for this predominantly synanthropic species would be of a wide, almost random, scatter. The map presented here, in contrast, shows a general coastal distribution and a clumped pattern centred on the regions around Fifeshire, Yorkshire, Cambridgeshire, Bedfordshire and the home counties. The clumping is likely to be the result of collecting bias, and *C. convexus* should be expected to occur throughout the British Isles in synanthropic habitats.

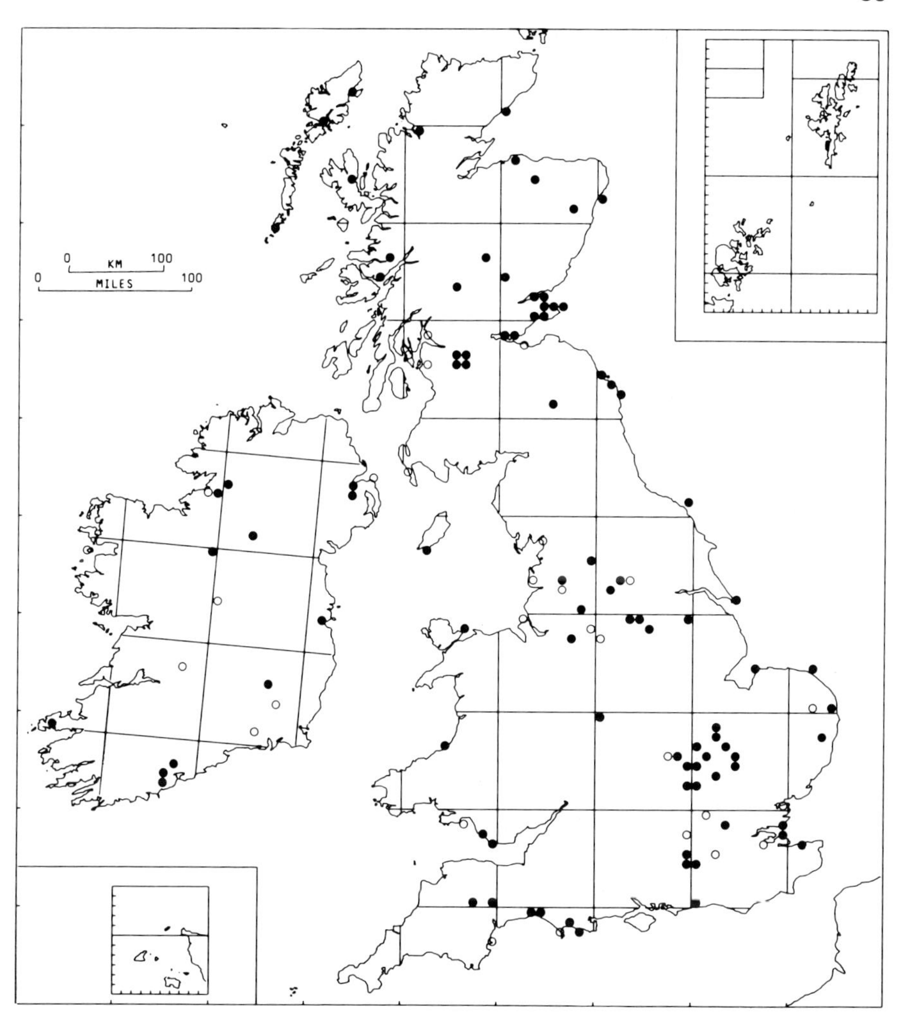

CYLISTICUS CONVEXUS

Number of records received: 158

England:	87 records	(55%)
Wales:	7 records	(4%)
Scotland:	42 records	(27%)
Isle of Man:	1 record	(<1%)
Ireland:	21 records	(13%)
Eire:	16 records	(10%)
Northern Ireland:	5 records	(3%)

Number of 10 km squares in which recorded:	122	
Number (%) of records with some habitat data:	119	(75%)
Number (%) of records from 1970 onwards:	124	(78%)

PORCELLIO DILATATUS Brandt

Porcellio dilatatus is a large, broad species with, especially in adult specimens, a characteristically rounded tip to the telson. The dorsal surface is distinctly tuberculate, although the tubercles are more rounded and broad-based than in *Porcellio scaber*. The whole animal is a dull, dusty-brown colour; it appears that *P. dilatatus* does not occur in the variety of colour forms found in *P. scaber*.

Habitat data

Only 39 (54%) of the 72 records of this species included information on habitat; thus, the following figures are based on a small sample.

A (39 records): Inland 67%, Coastal 33%.
B (39 records): Rural 59%, Suburban/village 28%, Urban 13%.
C (39 records): Building, inside 26%, Building, outside 18%, Garden 15%, Grassland, ungrazed 15%, Sea 8%.

It is usual to find *P. dilatatus* in small numbers but at a few sites it is abundant, eg in some buildings, especially ruins, and on chalk downland in Bedfordshire. Here it was taken in a fenced area from which rabbits and grazing stock had been excluded. Many of the records are from obviously synanthropic sites, but several have every appearance of being natural occurrences, eg on the downland in Bedfordshire, on chalk cliffs at Lulworth, Dorset, and at 2 sea-shore sites in Ireland at Miltown Malbay, Clare, and Castle Cove near Waterville, South Kerry.

Although never common, it appears that *P. dilatatus* was quite widely recorded earlier this century, especially in Ireland, where 60% of the records date from before 1925. Some records in the first half of the 20th century from Britain were the result of mis-identification, but it is probable that this species has declined due to a loss of suitable habitat in ruins and neglected outbuildings. It is certain that it is under-recorded in old gardens, glasshouses and farm outbuildings.

It has been spread by man to many parts of the world, where it has become naturalized, but its range is greatly extended to the north by being able to survive in glasshouses, eg in Reykjavik, Iceland, and in Oslo and Trondheim, Norway (Meinertz 1950). Vandel (1962) considered that it originated in the area of the western Mediterranean, but it is now known from most European countries.

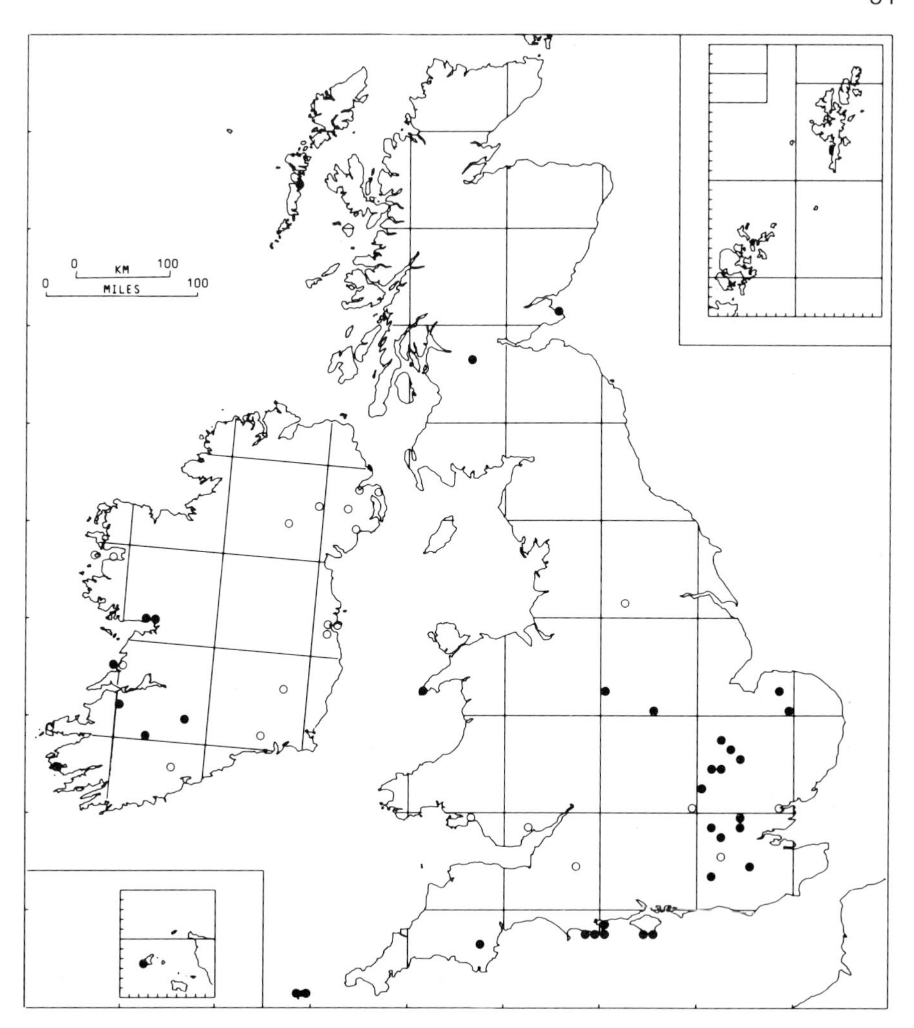

PORCELLIO DILATATUS

Number of records received: 72

England:	41 records	(57%)
Wales:	4 records	(6%)
Scotland:	3 records	(4%)
Channel Islands:	1 record	(1%)
Ireland:	23 records	(32%)
Eire:	18 records	(25%)
Northern Ireland:	5 records	(7%)

Number of 10 km squares in which recorded:	60	
Number (%) of records with some habitat data:	39	(54%)
Number (%) of records from 1970 onwards:	41	(57%)

PORCELLIO LAEVIS Latreille

This is a large, broad species, brown to light grey in colour, and with a smooth, shiny dorsal surface. The exopods are long and flattened but this feature is not as distinctive as the keys might suggest. When fully grown, *Porcellio laevis* is larger than other species of *Porcellio*.

Habitat data

Only 24 (58%) of the 41 records of this species include information on habitat; thus, the following figures are based on a small sample.

A (24 records): Coastal 50%, Inland 50%.
B (24 records): Suburban/village 58%, Rural 25%, Urban 17%.
C (24 records): Garden 54%, Waste ground 17%.
D (18 records): Compost/refuse heap 56%, Dung heap 17%, Hay (or other) stack 11%.

The present-day distribution of *P. laevis* shows a thin scatter of records with slight groupings in eastern England and near Dublin. It is a distinctive species but at present appears to be rare; this is incongruous when one considers the number of early records. Templeton (1836) listed only 5 species of woodlice in Ireland, one of which was *P. laevis*; Bate and Westwood (1868) stated that it 'occurs commonly in stable-litter'; according to Scharff, it was fairly common in the Dublin area in the 1890s (Pack Beresford & Foster 1911); and Webb and Sillem (1906) recorded it from the home counties and counties Dublin and Galway. There are very few records of woodlice from archaeological deposits but one is of *P. laevis*, from a late 13th century infill pit at Stonar, East Kent (Girling 1979). Although circumstantial, this evidence suggests that *P. laevis* was formerly more common.

It has been recorded mainly from compost, dung and straw heaps, farm outbuildings and municipal refuse tips. The only record away from a synanthropic association was at the base of a sea cliff at Howth, Dublin. Although the typical habitats of *P. laevis* have not been particularly well worked, it seems unlikely that one of the largest and most distinctive species could have been consistently overlooked by contributors to the Scheme. A possible explanation for the apparent decline of this species, in view of its frequent occurrence in dung heaps, is the progressive loss of horses from the urban and agricultural scene during this century. This fact, coupled with greater tidiness and hygiene in animal housing on farms, may provide an answer, but more surveys of farm buildings and dung heaps are needed to establish the occurrence of this species and also *Porcellio dilatatus* and *Porcellionides pruinosus*.

It is widespread in warmer parts of the world, where it has been spread by man, and occurs as far north as Denmark and southern Sweden in association with buildings, especially farms. Vandel (1962) considered it to have originated in the area of the Mediterranean.

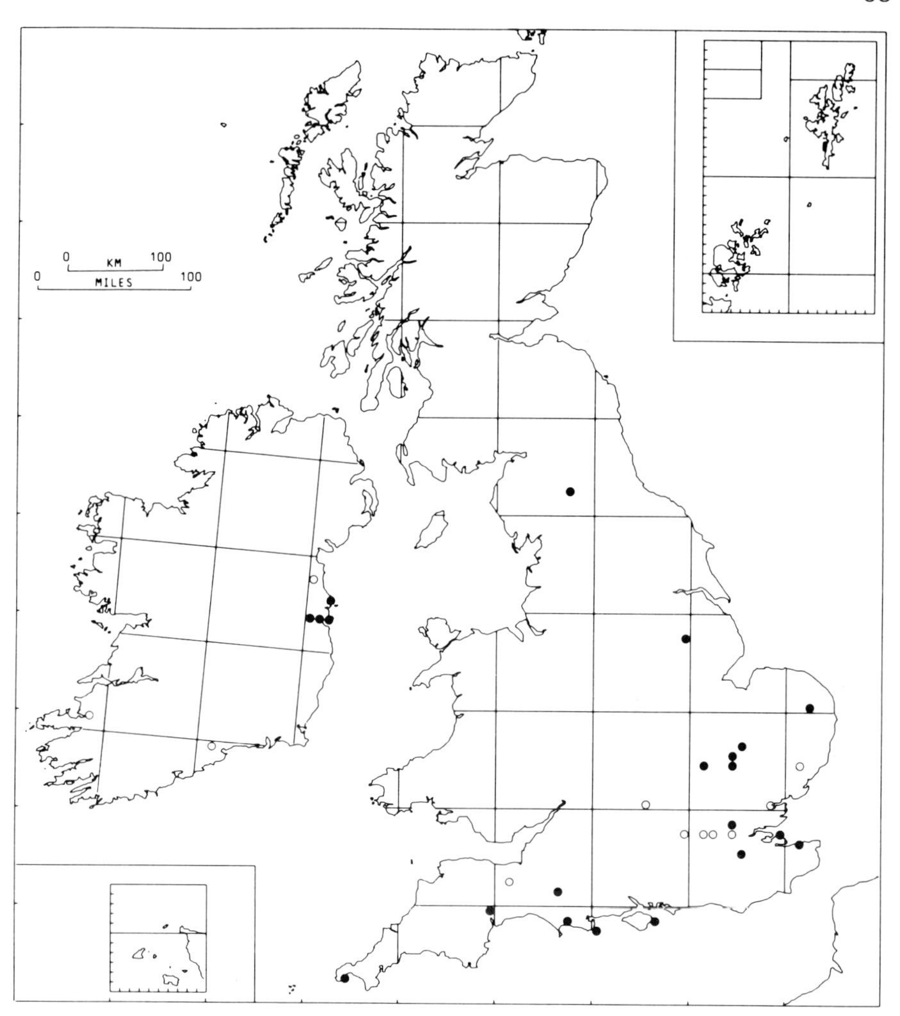

PORCELLIO LAEVIS

Number of records received: 41

England:	28 records	(68%)
Ireland:	13 records	(32%)
Eire:	13 records	(32%)

Number of 10 km squares in which recorded:	32	
Number (%) of records with some habitat data:	24	(58%)
Number (%) of records from 1970 onwards:	26	(63%)

PORCELLIO SCABER Latreille

Porcellio scaber is a medium to large, compact, rough-surfaced woodlouse, typically a deep slate-blue in colour in the male, but with females and juveniles paler and mottled. Brick-orange, brown and other colour forms are frequent. Often there is an orange flush on the most basal section of the antennae. In habitat range, it overlaps with 2 superficially similar species, *Porcellio spinicornis* and *Trachelipus rathkei*. From the former, it can usually be distinguished by not having a yellow marked pereon and black pleon, and from *T. rathkei*, by having only 2 pairs of pleopodal lungs, not 5.

It is probably our second most abundant and widespread species, after *Oniscus asellus*. It occurs in every vice-county in England and Wales and has been recorded in all the Scottish vice-counties, except Selkirk and the Clyde Isles. In Ireland, it is equally ubiquitous, occurring in all vice-counties. It has been recorded from 62% of the 10 km squares and 24% of all records received by the survey were of this species.

Habitat data

A (4669 records): Inland 54%, Coastal 46%.
B (4662 records): Rural 74%, Suburban/village 19%, Urban 7%.
C (4678 records): Garden 11%, Woodland, open herbs/grass 10%, Waste ground, more than 25% vegetation cover 9%, Grassland, lightly grazed 9%, Grassland, ungrazed 8%, Sea 7%, Building 7%.
D (2585 records): Shore, etc, 19%, Roadside verge 18%, Walls 16%, Natural cliff face 7%, Hedge 6%.
E (4599 records): Stones 42%, Dead wood 21%, Stone or brickwork 8%, Litter 7%.
H (a) Litter type (1418 records): Mixed grass/herbs 24%, Grass, species unknown 20%, Mixed deciduous 16%.
H (d) Soil/exposed rock (1693 records): Non-calcareous 53%, Calcareous 47%.

P. scaber is widely distributed and abundant, found by day under stones and dead wood in a wide range of 1st and 2nd Order Habitats, but particularly in gardens, marginal grassland and open woodland.

At first sight, *P. scaber* and *O. asellus* appear to show very similar habitat preferences. *P. scaber* is, however, much more common than *O. asellus* in sand dunes, in salt marshes and in the splash zone of the sea-shore, perhaps showing a marked tolerance of salt. It is much less common than *O. asellus* in the wet 2nd Order Habitats, eg dry watercourse bed, with 17% of all isopod records versus 28% for *O. asellus*. The subjective impression of most observers is that *P. scaber* is much more common on dry heaths, but *heather*, which would seem the best indicator on the survey card of dry heath, yielded for *P. scaber* only 26% of all isopod records, as compared to 40% for *O. asellus*! The impression that *P. scaber* occurs in drier and more open situations than *O. asellus* was not clearly borne out in the survey, and there was rather little difference in the preference of microsites. *P. scaber* is well known for its tendency to live up trees in the summer: 50% of records of all species from the bark of living trees were of *P. scaber*. Its population biology has been studied by Davis (1984). It is, with *O. asellus*, a minor pest of young plants in glasshouses and flower beds (Sutton & Coghill 1979).

Overseas, the species is native to western Europe, but it has proved probably the most successful woodlouse colonizer, occurring from Iceland to South America and South Africa.

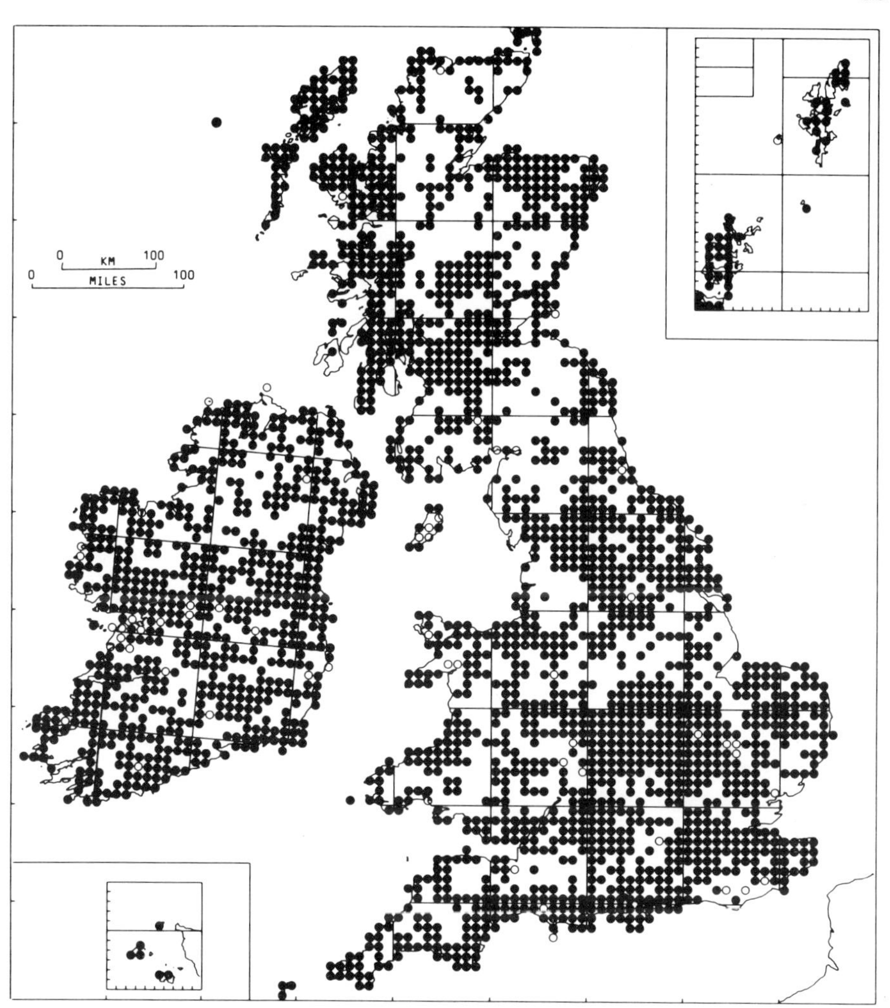

PORCELLIO SCABER

Number of records received: 5361

England:	2788 records	(52%)
Wales:	377 records	(7%)
Scotland:	1142 records	(22%)
Isle of Man:	17 records	(<1%)
Channel Islands:	18 records	(<1%)
Ireland:	1019 records	(19%)
Eire:	896 records	(17%)
Northern Ireland:	123 records	(2%)

Number of 10 km squares in which recorded:	2400	
Number (%) of records with some habitat data:	4678	(87%)
Number (%) of records from 1970 onwards:	5006	(93%)

PORCELLIO SPINICORNIS Say

Porcellio spinicornis is a very distinctively and attractively marked species; the head is always blackish, the body has a dark dorso-median stripe between 2 rows of yellow marks, and the sides of the body are mottled with paler brown. It can be confused with *Oniscus asellus* or *Porcellio scaber*. *P. spinicornis* is very active and can run much more rapidly than either of the above species. It is largely confined to stone walls and buildings.

Habitat data

A (360 records): Inland 62%, Coastal 38%.
B (361 records): Rural 61%, Suburban/village 29%, Urban 10%.
C (362 records): Building, outside 29%, Garden 20%, Building, inside 13%, Grassland, ungrazed & lightly grazed 13%, Waste ground 9%, Cereal crops 6%.
D (260 records): Wall with mortar 52%, Dry stone wall 24%, Road/path 6%, Quarry 5%.
E (348 records): Stone or brickwork 45%, Stones 36%, Dead wood 5%.
F (a) Building (123 records): Ruin 41%, Uninhabited/outbuilding 34%, Inhabited/public 24%, Greenhouse/unheated 1%.
G (357 records): Full daylight 87%, Dark 9%, Half-light, etc, 4%.
H (d) Soil/exposed rock (156 records): Calcareous 66%, Non-calcareous 34%.
I (a) Location of animal, horizon (283 records): Less than 3 m above ground 46%, On ground surface 42%, More than 3 m above ground 8%.
I (b) Position (123 records): In crevice 73%, In open 27%.

The records of *P. spinicornis* probably show greater recorder bias than those of any other large species. Because of its preference for inaccessible microsites in crevices in the stonework of walls and buildings, it is often difficult to find by day, although at night it is very conspicuous on the surface. The available records for England show it to be widespread in the Cotswolds and the limestone Pennines but sparse elsewhere and absent from the extreme south-west and most of the home counties. It is sparse in most of Wales and west Scotland, but is widespread in east Scotland and much of Northumberland, often occurring at considerable altitudes. In Ireland, it has been recorded infrequently, occurring chiefly in the south. The British Isles distribution thus seems to have a north-eastern, anti-Atlantic tendency similar to that noted for France (Vandel 1962). The records from natural sites (limestone cliffs and screes, and chalk cliffs in England, and eskers in Ireland), although few in number, may well represent true native sites.

P. spinicornis is frequently seen in large numbers at night on calcareous or mortared walls and buildings; characteristically, it will be seen on the coping or upper parts of a wall, while *P. scaber* will be lower down on the sides, suggesting that it can survive by day in microsites in the upper parts of the wall which are more liable to desiccation than those occupied by *P. scaber*. *P. spinicornis* in Ireland, Scotland and Wales is especially associated with ecclesiastical buildings and ruins. Although often abundant on dry stone walls made of limestone, it is rarely found on walls of non-calcareous rock, unless these are mortared.

P. spinicornis is recorded from central and northern France, northwards to a line from Trondheim to Leningrad, eastwards to the Ukraine and southwards to northern Italy; it is absent from south-west France and the Iberian Peninsula and most of the Mediterranean. It has been spread by man to Canada and the United States of America.

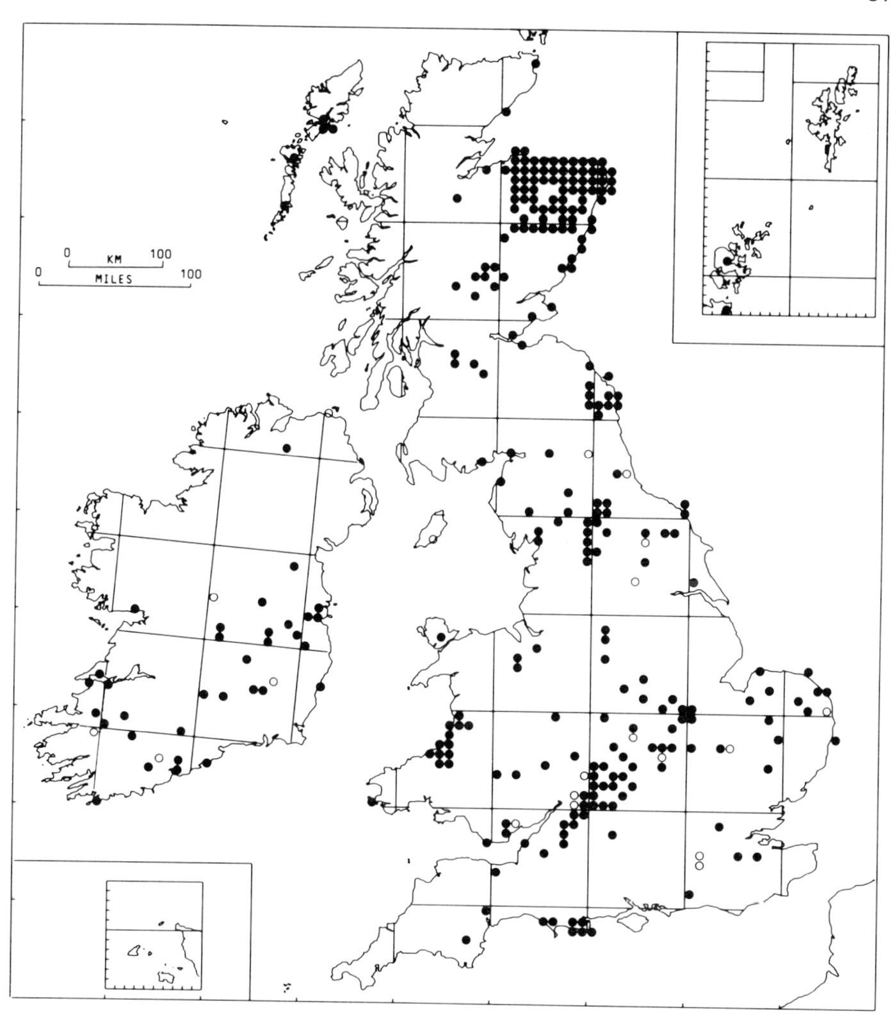

PORCELLIO SPINICORNIS

Number of records received: 398

England:	196 records	(49%)
Wales:	24 records	(6%)
Scotland:	140 records	(35%)
Isle of Man:	1 record	(<1%)
Ireland:	37 records	(10%)
Eire:	35 records	(9%)
Northern Ireland:	2 records	(<1%)

Number of 10 km squares in which recorded:	297	
Number (%) of records with some habitat data:	362	(91%)
Number (%) of records from 1970 onwards:	373	(94%)

PORCELLIONIDES CINGENDUS (Kinahan)

Porcellionides cingendus is somewhat similar in general appearance and behaviour to *Philoscia muscorum*, with which it is commonly associated, but is smaller and can be distinguished by its narrower, more parallel-sided body, matt (not shiny) surface, and speckled, dull, yellowish- to reddish-brown or grey colouring. It is very active, but does not move quite as fast as *P. muscorum*.

Habitat data

A (321 records): Coastal 74%, Inland 26%.
B (320 records): Rural 80%, Suburban/village 18%, Urban 2%.
C (321 records): Grassland, ungrazed 17%, Grassland, other 12%, Sea & Estuary 10%, Building, outside 10%, Garden 9%, Waste ground 8%, Woodland 7%, Scrubland 6%.
D (194 records): Natural cliff face 22%, Roadside verge 14%, Shore, etc, 13%, Embankment/cutting 10%, Dry stone wall 9%, Road/path 5%.
E (320 records): Stones 52%, Litter 20%, Tussocks 13%, Dead wood 5%.
I (a) Location of animal, horizon (206 records): On ground surface 58%, In litter 25%, Less than 3 m above ground 14%.

The distribution of this species is of a characteristic Atlantic and Lusitanian type. In Ireland, it occurs over much of the south-west, but also extends up the east coast to St John's Point, Down (its most northerly station in the world). In south-west England and south Wales, where it reaches as far north as the Dyfi estuary, it is predominantly coastal (although it has been found up to 13 km inland as far north as the Teifi valley). There is an outlying station in the Isle of Man, and it occurs over an extensive inland area in West Sussex and Surrey. This distribution has many elements in common with that of such plants as *Sibthorpia europaea* or *Dryopteris aemula*, or the snail *Cochlicella acuta* (Müller) with which *P. cingendus* often occurs. Climatic factors such as low winter temperatures presumably limit its distribution, which in the British Isles, as was noted in France by Legrand (1949), seems only rarely to cross the +5°C January mean isotherm. However, its absence from some areas such as north Wales, where it has been extensively searched for, is unexplained. The outlying records in West Sussex and Surrey are mainly in the area of generally oceanic climate sheltered from high wind exposure in the Weald. Paradoxically, this area is also favourable for a southern and eastern species, *Ligidium hypnorum*.

In England and Wales, it is most often found in grassland, scrub or open woodland in tussocks or in litter, but in Ireland it is common in a much greater range of habitats and microsites, being especially frequent under stones in coastal grassland. In some parts of south-west Ireland, it appears to be the commonest species of woodlouse. In West Sussex and Surrey, besides occurring abundantly in characteristic litter and grassland sites, it also occurs in wet alder carr in the same microsites as *Ligidium hypnorum*. Throughout most of its range, *P. cingendus* is very frequently associated with *Philoscia muscorum*; limited observations at night suggest that, to a greater extent than this species, *P. cingendus* remains in the same microsites in the dark as it is found in during the day.

Outside the British Isles, the species has been recorded only from the Atlantic coastal regions of Europe between Lisbon in Portugal and St Lunaire in Brittany.

[In 1983, A O Chater recorded *P. cingendus* at several additional localities in 10 km squares 51/00, 04, 12, 13, 14, 23, 33.]

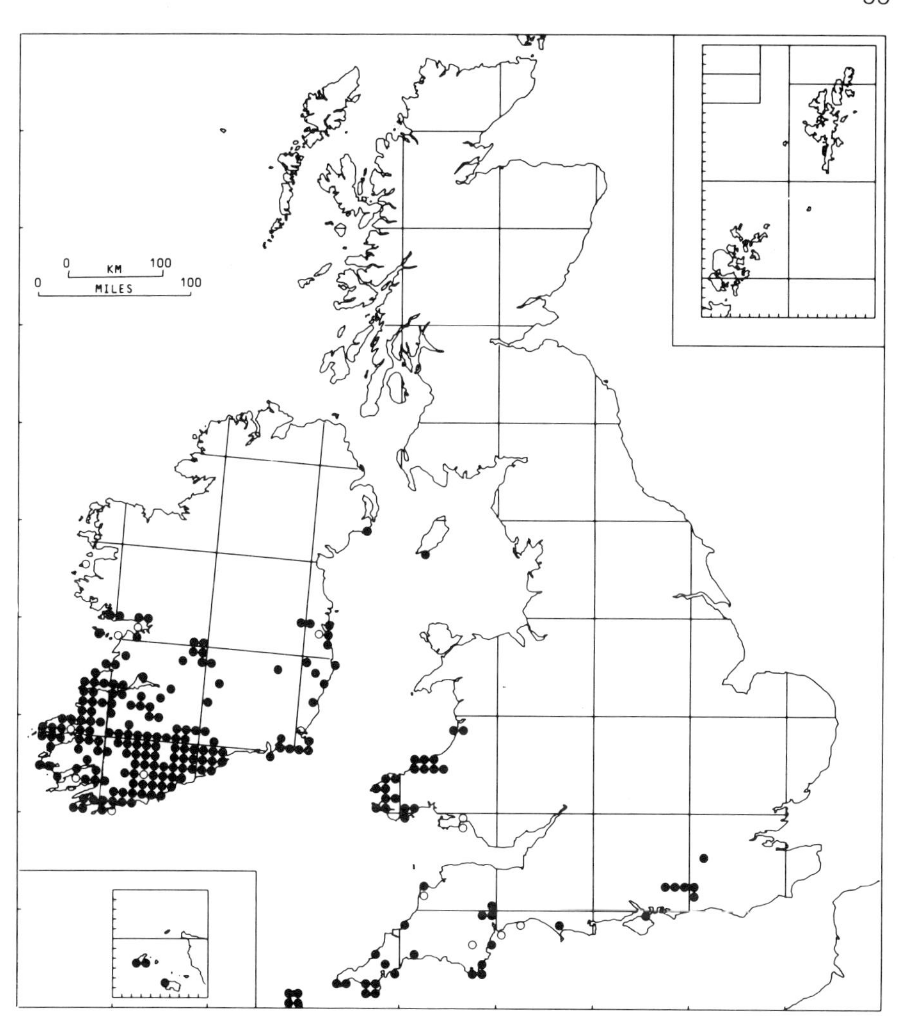

PORCELLIONIDES CINGENDUS

Number of records received: 376

England:	84 records	(22%)
Wales:	40 records	(11%)
Isle of Man:	1 record	(<1%)
Channel Islands:	4 records	(1%)
Ireland:	247 records	(66%)
Eire:	245 records	(65%)
Northern Ireland:	2 records	(<1%)

Number of 10 km squares in which recorded:	233	
Number (%) of records with some habitat data:	321	(85%)
Number (%) of records from 1970 onwards:	327	(87%)

PORCELLIONIDES PRUINOSUS (Brandt)

The purplish-brown colour, pruinose (dusty-looking) bloom on the surface and very pale legs make this species immediately recognizable in the field; it is only likely to be confused with juvenile *Porcellio laevis*. The bloom is lost when preserved in alcohol. In life, *Porcellionides pruinosus* is quite unlike *Porcellionides cingendus*; Vandel (1962) placed the 2 species in different sub-genera.

Habitat data

A (165 records): Inland 78%, Coastal 22%.
B (165 records): Rural 50%, Suburban/village 37%, Urban 13%.
C (165 records): Garden 33%, Building 21%, Waste ground 19%, Grassland 9%, Arable, cereal crops 8%, Arable, other crops 4%. Records from synanthropic sites 65%.
D (118 records): Dung heap 31%, Compost/refuse heap 29%, Flower bed 8%, Walls (stone & brick) 6%, Quarry 6%, Hedge 5%, Roadside verge & Embankment/cutting 5%. Records from synanthropic sites 94%.
E (157 records): Dung 22%, Stones 21%, Human rubbish/garbage 17%, Dead wood 11%, Stone or brickwork 8%, Litter 6%.

A few records were from sites which cannot be considered to be synanthropic, but the overall impression is of a species which thrives in a small range of habitat types created by man: dung and compost heaps, outbuildings, especially stables and other animal housing, and glasshouses. It can disperse from such sites and may be able to survive away from them, for example in garden flower beds, in arable fields, in hedge bottoms and on roadside verges.

Surveys of dung heaps in some areas have revealed this species in about 30% of the heaps examined. The species is clearly under-recorded and will probably be found to occur in dung heaps, etc, throughout much of southern Britain. In Scotland, it has been found abundantly inside farm buildings around Fife and almost certainly occurs more widely.

Early writers differed about the commonness of this species: Kinahan (1857) and Bate and Westwood (1868) considered it to be one of the commonest British woodlice, but Scharff (1894) and Pack Beresford and Foster (1911) disagreed. The evidence from published records and museum collections tends to support the view that *P. pruinosus* was not a common species in the 19th century. However, its association with dung and compost heaps and heated glasshouses, all of which are less plentiful than formerly, may have led to a decline in its occurrence, as with *Porcellio laevis*.

The status of *P. pruinosus* in the British Isles is uncertain, but its synanthropic nature suggests that it is an introduction. However, if it is an introduction, it may be an ancient one. Girling (1979) recorded a calcified head of this species from the excavation of a Roman site at Southwark in London. She speculated that *P. pruinosus* existed in Britain during historic times and was possibly indigenous, having survived in naturally occurring niches until many more habitats became available through the activities of man. Although recorded in a few non-synanthropic sites, there is no consistency of natural habitat type as with, for example, *Porcellio spinicornis*.

Vandel (1962) considered it to have originated in the Mediterranean region and to have been spread by association with man to many parts of the world.

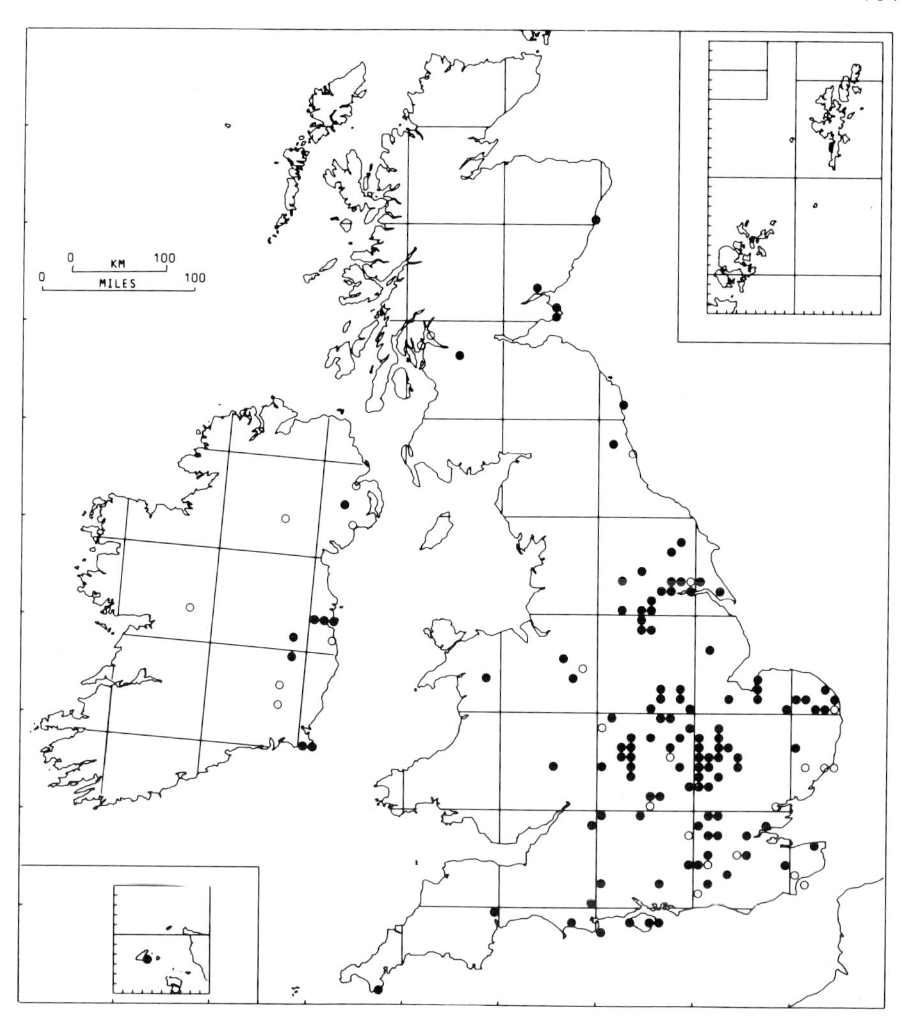

PORCELLIONIDES PRUINOSUS

Number of records received: 214

England:	177 records	(83%)
Wales:	1 record	(<1%)
Scotland:	14 records	(7%)
Channel Islands:	2 records	(1%)
Ireland:	20 records	(9%)
Eire:	17 records	(8%)
Northern Ireland:	3 records	(1%)

Number of 10 km squares in which recorded:	148	
Number (%) of records with some habitat data:	165	(77%)
Number (%) of records from 1970 onwards:	176	(82%)

TRACHELIPUS RATHKEI (Brandt)

Although *T. rathkei* is distinctively marked, with a regular longitudinal patterning of light colour on a ground of grey-brown flecked with off-white, specimens of *Porcellio scaber* have frequently been mistaken for it. In live specimens, the presence of 5 pairs of pleopodal lungs is distinctive; they show as large white patches and can be seen with a hand lens. *Porcellio* species have only 2 pairs of pleopodal lungs.

Habitat data

A (70 records): Inland 93%, Coastal 7%.
B (70 records): Rural 71%, Suburban/village 19%, Urban 10%.
C (69 records): Waste ground 20%, Grassland, ungrazed 17%, Grassland, other 16%, Garden 14%, Woodland 13%, Fen & Carr 13%.
D (35 records): Roadside verge & Embankment/cutting 23%, Flower bed 15%, Woodland ride 11%.
E (66 records): Litter 26%, Stones 23%, Dead wood 18%.
H (e) (Soil) (45 records): Clayey 40%, Heavy clay 20%, Peat 15%, Loam 15%.

T. rathkei was considered by Collinge (1944a) to be widely distributed in Britain and also to have occurred once in Ireland (Collinge 1918a). Re-examination of early British material purporting to be this species, mainly in the W E Collinge collection at the Yorkshire Museum (Harding 1977), has proved many records to be erroneous. Doogue and Harding (1982) considered the Irish record to be unreliable.

The occurrence of *T. rathkei* in Britain, as revealed by the survey, is puzzling. In Northamptonshire, the north-western corner of its distribution, it is common in disused opencast ironstone workings, occurring in ill-drained grassy waste ground, re-seeded pasture and the rides and firebreaks of plantations, on clayey soils derived from the Jurassic strata stripped as overburden in the mining process. Further east, in Huntingdonshire, it occurs in the few remaining rough grasslands and small woods on clayey soils; it is common in the grassland and scrub surrounding Monks Wood Experimental Station and in the large clearings in Monks Wood National Nature Reserve. Nearby at Woodwalton Fen National Nature Reserve, it is common in fen litter and in open areas of carr.

To the south of the Northamptonshire/Huntingdonshire block, there is an irregular scatter of records, probably as a result of under-recording. However, thorough surveys in Bedfordshire, Surrey and Kent have resulted in comparatively few records. These southern records have mainly been from waste ground and damp grassland, but there were also a few from gardens. In Kent, it has been recorded in a few grassy coastal sites. The westernmost records are from the banks of the River Thames, near Wallingford, Berkshire, and from Wytham Hill, Berkshire. Girling (1979) suggested that *T. rathkei* occurred (as calcium carbonate replacement fossils) in archaeological deposits from south and east England and south Wales. However, the evidence for suggesting that these were *T. rathkei* rather than *P. scaber* was inconclusive.

T. rathkei is widely recorded in central and eastern Europe, north to southern Scandinavia and eastern Denmark. Its western limit is England and the Channel Islands (records in Vandel 1960a), and it occurs only in northern and eastern France. In France, it is a species mainly of river valley grasslands. It is infrequently recorded in synanthropic situations but has apparently been widely spread by man outside Europe. In North America, it has become a characteristic component of the fauna of hickory, cottonwood and hemlock woodlands.

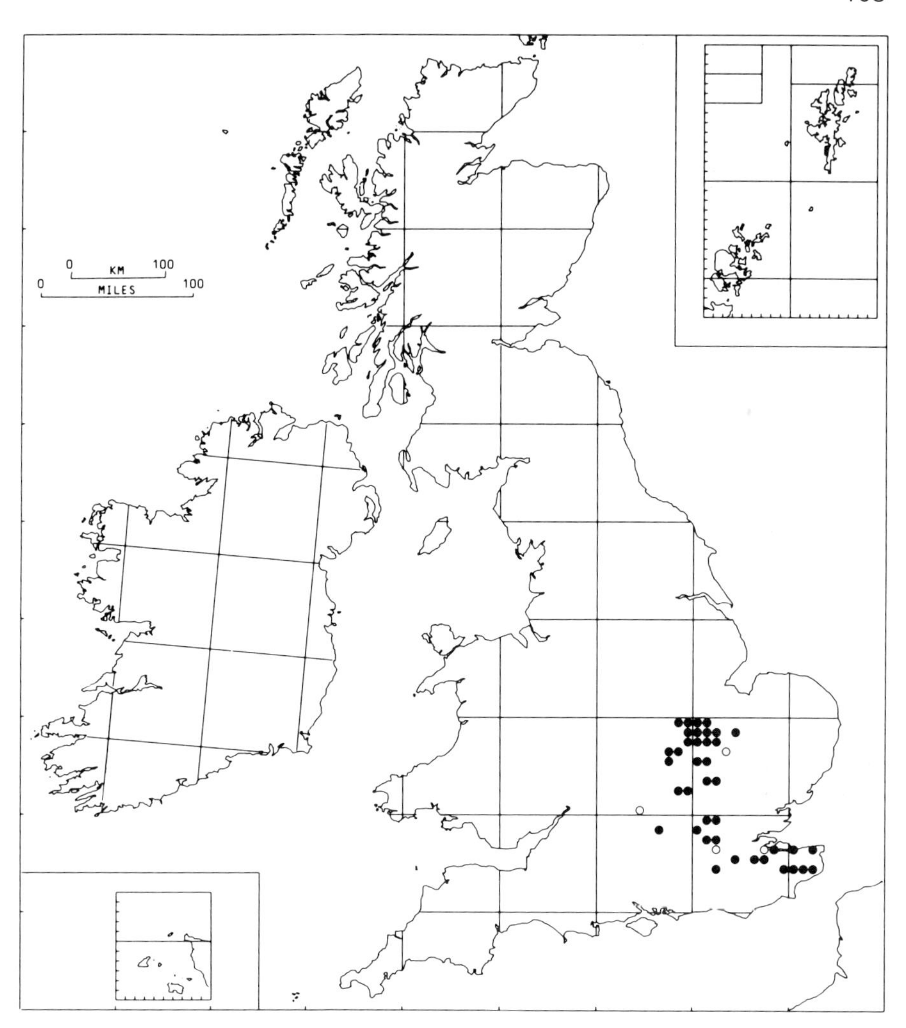

TRACHELIPUS RATHKEI

Number of records received: 84

England: 84 records (100%)

Number of 10 km squares in which recorded: 43
Number (%) of records with some habitat data: 70 (83%)
Number (%) of records from 1970 onwards: 72 (86%)

V. HABITAT ACCOUNTS

The following section describes the assemblages of species recorded from the major habitat types in Section C (1st Order Habitats) of the recording card (Figure 2). Table 4 lists the species recorded from selected habitat features in Section D (2nd Order Habitats).

1st Order Habitats In the account of each major habitat type, the percentage stated for each species was calculated from the number of records of the species from that habitat against the total number of records of all species from the habitat. On reviewing the analysis of data, it has become clear that the original survey did not take account of the variety of coastal habitats and their importance for woodlice. Coastal habitat types have therefore been treated separately without percentages for each species, except *Salt marsh* and *Sand dunes* which were included in the 1st Order Habitats section.

2nd Order Habitats Only those habitat features for which more than 500 records were received have been included in Table 4. Records from *Quarry face* and *Quarry floor* have been combined. Percentages in Table 4 should be compared with the percentage of records with habitat data for each species in Table 1.

Five species (*Armadillidium vulgare, Oniscus asellus, Philoscia muscorum, Porcellio scaber* and *Trichoniscus pusillus*) occurred in all major 1st Order Habitats. Records of these 5 eurytopic species combined made up 80% of all records received by the survey and 81% of records with habitat data.

1st Order Habitats

MARSH

Four types of marsh were defined in the survey, one of which, *Salt marsh*, is described under Coastal Habitats. The remaining types (*Fen* 203 records, *Carr* 151 records, *Bog* 67 records) were infrequently recorded. Twenty species were found.

From these 421 records, there appear to be 4 elements in the woodlouse fauna of marshes. Of the soil dwelling species, *Trichoniscus pusillus* (26%) was common in all 3 types, *Haplophthalmus mengei* (2%) was more common in fens and bogs than in carrs, *Trichoniscus pygmaeus* (2%) was recorded more commonly in bogs than in fens and carrs, and *Trichoniscoides albidus* (<1%) was recorded in a few fens. Tussocky vegetation in fens and bogs was the most frequently recorded marsh location for *Philoscia muscorum* (19%), but this species and *Ligidium hypnorum* (6%), *Porcellionides cingendus* (2%, mainly in Ireland) and *Trachelipus rathkei* (2%) were characteristic of fen and carr litter. Dead wood and artificial piles of dead vegetation (eg that cleared from fen dykes) provided sites for *Oniscus asellus* (19%), *Porcellio scaber* (12%) and *Haplophthalmus danicus* (<1%), with *Armadillidium vulgare* (5%) occurring in drier sites such as dykeside banks.

Only *L. hypnorum* and *T. rathkei* can be considered to be distinctively marshland species, although both occur in other habitat types. Further surveys could establish whether *H. mengei* and *T. albidus* are widely associated with peat soils in fens and carrs.

CAVE/WELL/TUNNEL

This habitat feature was designed to record the subterranean fauna. Habitat data were few (*Threshold* 39 records, *Dark zone* 24 records), although additional records from caves and mines were abstracted from the publications of the British Cave Research Association and its predecessors, but without habitat data. Eleven species were recorded.

In the British Isles there is no characteristic suite of species known only from subterranean sites, as there is in France and Spain. The only species recorded with any frequency in this habitat were *Androniscus dentiger* (50% of records from *Dark zone*, 30% overall) and *Oniscus asellus* (33% overall). The inclusion of habitat data from published records would greatly increase the frequency with which *A. dentiger* occurred in caves and mines. *Cylisticus convexus* has been recorded from several tunnels and underground drains, and *Haplophthalmus danicus* and *Trichoniscoides saeroeensis* have also been recorded from caves, etc. With so few records it is impossible to assess the importance of subterranean sites for these 3 species. Sheppard (1968) suggested that *T. saeroeensis* was an established member of the cave fauna, but subsequent records have shown it to be essentially a coastal species.

Several eurytopic species have been recorded from caves, etc, mainly in the *Threshold* zone: *Armadillidium vulgare* (4%), *Philoscia muscorum* (1%), *Porcellio scaber* (12%) and *Trichoniscus pusillus* (5%). *Halophiloscia couchi* and *Ligia oceanica* were recorded from the *Threshold* of caves on the sea-shore.

BUILDING

Buildings and their immediate surroundings were well surveyed with 1595 records (*Inside* 332 records, *Outside* 1263 records). All the eurytopic species occurred in association with buildings. The faunas of *Building* and *Garden* have many similarities, although, with 20 species recorded, *Building* had 5 fewer species.

Many records from *Inside* buildings were from *Ruins* and *Outbuildings*. Such locations were important for records of *Porcellio spinicornis* (11%), *Porcellionides pruinosus* (3%), *Porcellio dilatatus* (2%) and *Armadillidium nasatum* (2%). The species most frequently recorded inside occupied dwelling-houses were *Porcellio scaber* (21%), *P. spinicornis, Armadillidium vulgare* (6%) and *A. nasatum*. Farm outbuildings, barns, stables, etc, provided records of *P. pruinosus, P. dilatatus* and *Porcellio laevis* (<1%), usually in straw and stable litter.

The *Outside* walls of buildings, particularly at the wall/soil interface, have been productive for records, there being some overlap with records from *Gardens*. *Oniscus asellus* (24%), *P. scaber* and *P. spinicornis* were recorded frequently and the few night-time records demonstrated that these species are often abundant, browsing on algae on the wall surface by night and hiding in crevices by day. In damper situations, *Trichoniscus pusillus* (9%), *Philoscia muscorum* (7%), *Androniscus dentiger* (5%) and *Trichoniscus pygmaeus* (2%) were recorded.

Glasshouses have a particularly distinctive fauna with many alien species (see page 17) occurring only in heated glasshouses, particularly in botanic gardens. *A. nasatum* was formerly widely recorded in commercial glasshouses, but recent records have been scarce. Sutton and Coghill (1979) described the control of woodlice in glasshouses.

GARDEN

Domestic gardens were the third most frequently recorded single feature in Section C (2323 records). Twenty-five species were recorded, including almost every native and naturalized species, the exceptions being *Armadillidium pictum, Armadillidium pulchellum* and the exclusively coastal species. A few records from churchyards were included under *Garden*.

Eurytopic species predominated: *Oniscus asellus* (23%), *Porcellio scaber* (22%), *Philoscia muscorum* (11%), *Trichoniscus pusillus* (9%) and *Armadillidium vulgare* (9%). Several features of gardens in Section D amplify the overall figures. *Rockery* (303 records) was important for records of *Androniscus dentiger* (6%), *Armadillidium depressum* (1%), *Armadillidium nasatum* (<1%), *Porcellio laevis* (<1%) and *Trichoniscoides albidus* (<1%). *Flower bed* (282 records) was important for *A. dentiger, Platyarthrus hoffmannseggi* (4%), *Porcellionides pruinosus* (2%), *Cylisticus convexus* (<1%), *Porcellio dilatatus* (<1%) and *Trachelipus rathkei* (<1%). *Garden compost/refuse heaps* were important for *P. pruinosus, P. dilatatus* and *P.*

laevis, and also *A. dentiger*, *Eluma purpurascens* (<1%) and *Haplophthalmus danicus* (<1%).

The richness of the soil fauna of gardens was demonstrated with all the non-coastal, soil-dwelling species being recorded. Walls in gardens frequently provided sites for *Porcellio spinicornis* (3%). *Porcellionides cingendus* (1%) was recorded from a few gardens in western Ireland. Although placed under *Arable, Market gardens* (44 records) had more in common with *Garden* than with other arable types; only 11 species were recorded, with *A. dentiger, A. nasatum, C. convexus* and *P. pruinosus* recorded at above average frequency.

WASTE GROUND

The habitat was defined in the *Instructions to collectors* (Appendix 4) but, despite this, records were almost certainly incorrectly allocated to it. The total of records (2588) was divided unequally with twice the number of records from sites with *More than 25% of vegetation cover* (2368) than from sites with *Less than 25% of vegetation cover* (1220). It seems that many marginal habitats (*Roadside verge, Embankment,* etc) were entered under *Waste ground*, rather than under the appropriate adjacent land use type (*Grassland, Arable,* etc). Therefore, it is difficult to draw reliable conclusions about the characteristic fauna of this habitat type. Twenty-nine species were recorded from *Waste ground*.

The assemblage of eurytopic species was well represented: *Oniscus asellus* (23%), *Porcellio scaber* (19%), *Philoscia muscorum* (14%), *Trichoniscus pusillus* (13%) and *Armadillidium vulgare* (11%). Other species which occurred regularly were *Androniscus dentiger* (5%), *Platyarthrus hoffmannseggi* (2%), *Trichoniscus pygmaeus* (2%) and *Cylisticus convexus* (1%). A few species were recorded with above average frequency, constituting possibly a characteristic *Waste ground* fauna: *A. dentiger, C. convexus, Armadillidium depressum* (<1%), *Eluma purpurascens* (<1%), *Trachelipus rathkei* (<1%) and *Trichoniscoides albidus* (<1%).

ARABLE

Of the 4 truly *Arable* crop types, only *Cereal crops* were adequately recorded (439 records) with *Root crops* (18 records), *Fodder crops* (20 records) and *Grass ley* (91 records) poorly surveyed. A fifth type, *Market garden*, is dealt with under *Garden*. Eighteen species were recorded from the 4 types, of which *Oritoniscus flavus* (<1%) occurred only in *Grass ley*.

The common eurytopic species occurred in proportions similar to those recorded for *Waste ground*. The majority of records was from marginal 2nd Order Habitats (Section D) adjacent to arable land (*Hedge, Roadside verge, Embankment/cutting, Dry stone wall,* etc) or from *Dung heaps*, and therefore reflect the fauna of these marginal habitats rather than of arable crops themselves. The species associated with marginal habitats included *Porcellio spinicornis* (3%), *Haplophthalmus danicus* (3%), *Porcellionides pruinosus* (3%), *Armadillidium nasatum* (2%) and *Platyarthrus hoffmannseggi* (2%). These species were associated particularly with *Walls*, and stones and rubbish on *Roadside verges*. *P. pruinosus* and *Porcellio laevis* (1%) were recorded in *Dung heaps* or associated with dung spread on fields. Limited sampling of some arable crops as part of surveys of crop fauna suggests that few woodlice inhabit the vegetation or soil of arable fields permanently.

GRASSLAND

With 5530 records, *Grassland* was the most frequently recorded major habitat. The majority of records was from *Ungrazed* (2297) and *Lightly grazed* (2065), with markedly fewer records from *Heavily grazed* (776) and *Mown* (392).

Twenty-eight species were recorded, of which *Oniscus asellus* (23%), *Porcellio scaber* (20%), *Philoscia muscorum* (19%), *Trichoniscus pusillus* (13%) and *Armadillidium vulgare* (9%) were the most frequent. *Platyarthrus hoffmannseggi* (3%), *Androniscus dentiger* (2%), *Trichoniscus pygmaeus* (2%), *Haplophthalmus mengei* (1%) and *Porcellionides cingendus* (1%) also occurred regularly. *Grassland* is an important habitat for the occurrence of *P. muscorum, P. hoffmannseggi* and *Trachelipus rathkei* (<1%), with above average occurrences of each. During surveys in 1968–69, *P. muscorum* proved to be widespread and abundant in lowland calcareous grassland (P T Harding, unpublished). *P. hoffmannseggi* was normally found in association with ants, particularly under stones. In England, *Armadillidium pulchellum* (<1%) occurred mainly in screes in upland grassland, and *T. rathkei* was found mainly in ill-drained grassland on clayey soils. Detailed surveys of different grassland types have not been made, but would probably identify several distinct assemblages of species which it has not been possible to determine from the data collected by the survey.

SCRUBLAND

Scrubland was moderately well surveyed with 1178 records, of which 998 were from *Scrubland, open with herbs/grass* and 180 from *Scrubland, dense*.

Of the 24 species recorded, 4 were frequent: *Oniscus asellus* (26%), *Trichoniscus pusillus* (24%), *Philoscia muscorum* (16%) and *Porcellio scaber* (14%). Other species which occurred regularly were *Armadillidium vulgare* (6%), *Trichoniscus pygmaeus* (4%), *Androniscus dentiger* (2%), *Porcellionides cingendus* (2%) and *Haplophthalmus mengei* (1%).

Only 3 species were recorded in *Scrubland* with above average frequency: *T. pusillus, Armadillidium pictum* (<1%) and *Oritoniscus flavus* (<1%); *T. pusillus* occurred mainly in leaf litter, as in *Woodland.*

WOODLAND

Woodland was the second most frequently recorded major habitat (4618 records) and *Woodland, open with herbs/grass* was the most frequently recorded single feature in Section C (2382 records).

Although 26 species were recorded, only 4 were frequent: *Oniscus asellus* (32%), *Trichoniscus pusillus* (27%), *Porcellio scaber* (17%) and *Philoscia muscorum* (12%). Other species which occurred regularly were *Armadillidium vulgare* (3%), *Trichoniscus pygmaeus* (3%), *Androniscus dentiger* (1%), *Haplophthalmus danicus* (1%), *Haplophthalmus mengei* (1%) and *Ligidium hypnorum* (1%).

Woodland was an important habitat for *Armadillidium pictum* (<1%), *H. danicus, L. hypnorum* and *T. pusillus,* all of which had above average numbers of records. Leaf litter and the damp soil/litter interface were important habitats for woodlice in woodland and seem to have been sampled frequently (all *Litter* types 2837 records). The frequency with which *O. asellus* and *T. pusillus* occurred reflects the importance of leaf litter as a moisture-retaining habitat because both species are associated with more damp situations than, for example, *P. scaber.*

ACID HEATH/MOOR

Few records (511) were received for this habitat. Although 5 types were detailed on the card, records were mainly from *Grass/sedge/rush* (200 records), *Mixed* (162 records) and *Heather* (125 records). There were no records from *Vaccinium* (bilberry).

Only 15 species were recorded, of which the most frequent were *Oniscus asellus* (35%), *Porcellio scaber* (24%), *Trichoniscus pusillus* (17%) and *Philoscia muscorum* (14%). Other species included *Armadillidium vulgare* (4%), *Armadillidium pulchellum* (1%), *Porcellio spinicornis* (1%) and *Porcellionides cingendus* (1%). This habitat was important for only one species, *A.*

pulchellum, which occurred with above average frequency, mainly among screes from limestone outcrops and in small calcareous pockets in acidic grassland. Many of the other species, and particularly *A. vulgare*, were recorded in association with walls, buildings, and other synanthropic sites.

Coastal Habitats

SALT MARSH

Salt marshes form where silt accumulates in shallow tidal water, in the estuaries of rivers and behind dune systems and shingle ridges. Most species of woodlice appear to be unable to survive frequent inundation, so that salt marshes are not good areas for them. Despite this fact, 13 species were recorded. Woodlice occur on salt marshes almost exclusively in the strandline, although occasional specimens (mainly *Ligia oceanica, Porcellio scaber* and *Armadillidium album*) were found under isolated pieces of drift material in the upper parts, mainly in the Festucetum/Juncetum. *L. oceanica* was recorded very infrequently on the general salt marsh, usually associated with wooden piles or other artefacts.

Several rare species were characteristic of salt marsh strandlines—*A. album* (3%), *Miktoniscus patiencei* (3%) and *Trichoniscoides saeroeensis* (2%). At salt marsh sites in Dorset, South Hampshire and the Isle of Wight, *M. patiencei* and *Platyarthrus hoffmannseggi* (1%) were recorded regularly in association with ants just inland from the upper strandlines.

The species most frequently recorded on salt marshes were *Porcellio scaber* (29%), *Ligia oceanica* (18%), *Oniscus asellus* (14%), *Philoscia muscorum* (13%), *Armadillidium vulgare* (8%) and *Trichoniscus pusillus* (7%). Also recorded were *Porcellionides cingendus* (1%), *Cylisticus convexus* (<1%) and *Oritoniscus flavus* (<1%).

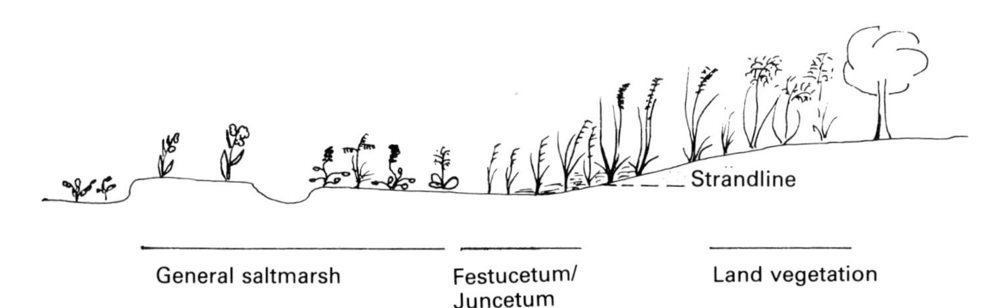

Figure 4 Diagrammatic profile of salt marsh

SAND DUNE

Although 20 species have been recorded from sand dunes (Table 3), only *Armadillidium vulgare, Philoscia muscorum* and *Porcellio scaber* were widespread and common. These 3 species have been the subject of studies on sand dunes at Spurn Head, South-east Yorkshire, which examined their role in the grassland ecology (Sunderland *et al.* 1976; Davis *et al.* 1977; Davis & Sutton 1978; Hassall & Sutton 1978; Davis 1984; Sutton *et al.* 1984). These studies, together with less detailed studies at Whiteford Burrows, Glamorgan (Cotton 1967; Harding 1971), have reinforced knowledge of the occurrence of woodlice on sand dunes gathered by the survey.

Porcellio scaber was almost always a very prominent member of the invertebrate fauna of dune systems. In the *Yellow dune* zone it was often the only species, although both *A. vulgare* and *P. muscorum* also occurred at some sites and in damp or windless conditions. *P. muscorum* was characteristic of tall, stabilised vegetation, particularly in the *Dune slack* and *Dense sward* zones. At some northern and western dune sites, *P. muscorum* was particularly abundant, outnumbering other species as at Murrough, Clare (Harding 1968b). *A. vulgare* was usually associated with areas dominated by marram grass (*Ammophila arenaria*) and often with shorter grassland with scattered marram grass.

Three other species occurred regularly on dune systems. *Armadillidium album* was found among sea drift material in the strandline, often at depths of 20–30 cm in sand. *A. vulgare* and *P. scaber* were also occasionally recorded in the strandline. *Platyarthrus hoffmannseggi* was recorded in association with ant nests in stabilised zones. *Trichoniscus pusillus* was recorded in all 5 habitats, usually in association with damp hollows, mossy areas, large pieces of concrete or decaying wood, but mainly in *Dune slacks*.

Oniscus asellus was recorded almost invariably in association with ruined buildings, decaying wood and other debris and rubbish. In Ireland, *Porcellionides cingendus* occurred on dunes, mainly in areas of dense grassy sward and in damp locations.

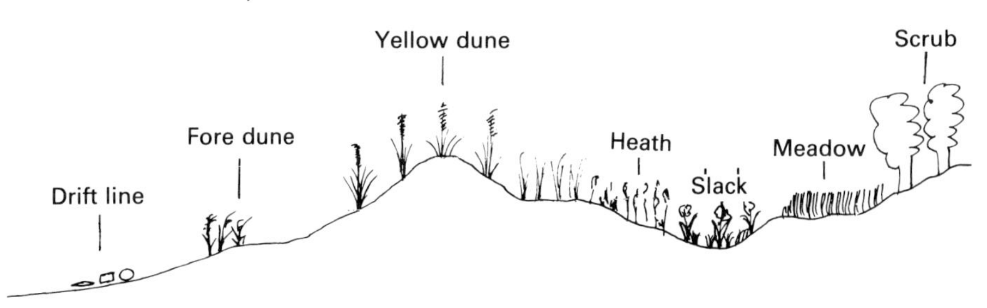

Figure 5 Diagrammatic profile of sand dune

Table 3 Percentage of records for each species in each habitat feature of sand dunes

	Androniscus dentiger	Armadillidium album	A. nasatum	A. pulchellum	A. vulgare	Cylisticus convexus	Eluma purpurascens	Haplophthalmus mengei	Ligia oceanica	Oniscus asellus	Philoscia muscorum	Platyarthrus hoffmannseggi	Porcellio dilatatus	P. scaber	P. spinicornis	Porcellionides cingendus	P. pruinosus	Trichoniscoides saeroeensis	Trichoniscus pusillus	T. pygmaeus	Total number of records	Total number of species
Bare sand	1	32	2	1	12		1		2	6	6	2		30		2			3		100	13
Tussocky		2			14		1	<1		10	16	3		44	<1	1		<1	5		149	12
Dense sward					15	<1	1	<1		9	24	2	<1	38		3	<1		6		195	12
Dune slack					25		1			10	24	4		29					6	1	83	8
Dune heath		2		2	20					9	20	3		37		2			5		56	9

SHINGLE

Shingle shores are widespread in the British Isles, forming substantial lengths of coastline, for example at Slapton Ley in South Devon, Chesil, Dorset, the south and east coasts of Sussex and East Kent and much of the coast of East Anglia. Shingle is often mixed with sand in varying quantities and, on the shores of some estuaries, with silt. Shingle banks and ridges, when fully developed, form wide, fairly flat-topped features with a zonation of vegetation from strandline plants (zone A) to maritime grassland with herbs (zone B). On the seaward side of zone A, the beach is devoid of vegetation. In some places, shingle builds up as an almost unvegetated bank against coastal grassland or other land vegetation.

The foreshore of shingle beaches, between mean high water mark (HWMN) and the extreme high water mark of spring tides (EHWMOS), where vegetation is absent may seem an improbable habitat for woodlice, but this was the typical situation in which *Stenophiloscia zosterae* occurred (Harding *et al.* 1980), and from which *Halophiloscia couchi* was also recorded.

Several species were recorded in zone A among the strandline and pioneer vegetation such as sea rocket (*Cakile maritima*), sea sandwort (*Honkenya peploides*) and sand couch-grass (*Elymus farctus*), including *Porcellio scaber, Armadillidium vulgare, Cylisticus convexus, Oniscus asellus* and *Philoscia muscorum*. Deeper in the shingle among damp soil derived from drift material, small species have been found, including *Trichoniscus pusillus, Trichoniscus pygmaeus, Trichoniscoides saeroeensis* and *Miktoniscus patiencei*.

Similar assemblages were recorded in zone B, but a more humus-rich soil develops deep in the shingle, in which *Haplophthalmus mengei, Androniscus dentiger* and *Buddelundiella cataractae* occurred.

Areas of shingle beaches and vegetated ridges have not been adequately sampled because special techniques are required, such as pitfall traps for *S. zosterae* and sieving and floatation for the deep-dwelling species, especially *B. cataractae*.

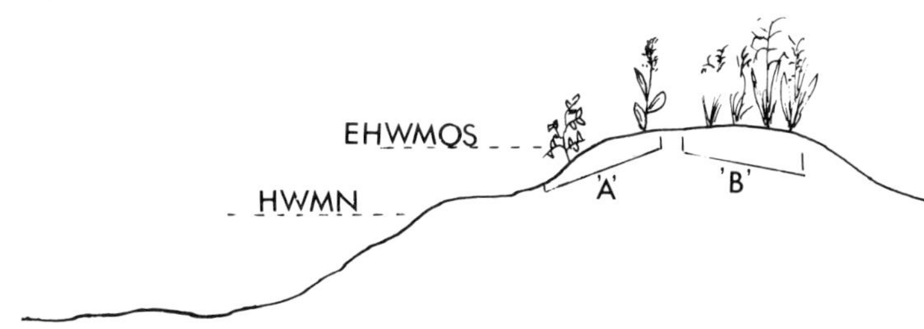

Figure 6 Diagrammatic profile of shingle beach

BOULDER BEACH

On exposed coasts where physical and geological factors permit, storm beaches have formed which are composed primarily of rounded stones and pebbles. In some instances, these have built up against cliffs or have formed round-topped banks reaching to or above high water mark. Nothing is known of the fauna below extreme high water mark because of the difficulty of sampling among the stones.

Just above extreme high water mark, the stones are stabilised by a sparse vegetation of strandline plants (zone A). In the top layers (h1) little was found, except for occasional specimens of *Porcellio scaber* and *Armadillidium vulgare*. Deeper down, where the humidity was higher and where there were fragments of soil (h2), *Oniscus asellus, Trichoniscus pusillus* and *Androniscus dentiger* occurred mainly in crevices. Deeper again (h3), where more soil had accumulated, soil-dwelling species occurred, including *Haplophthalmus mengei* and *Trichoniscus pygmaeus. Buddelundiella cataractae* also occurred in this horizon at Barry, Glamorgan.

The fauna of zone B was usually similar to that of vegetated cliffs or any other coastal grassland, depending on the conformation of the coastline.

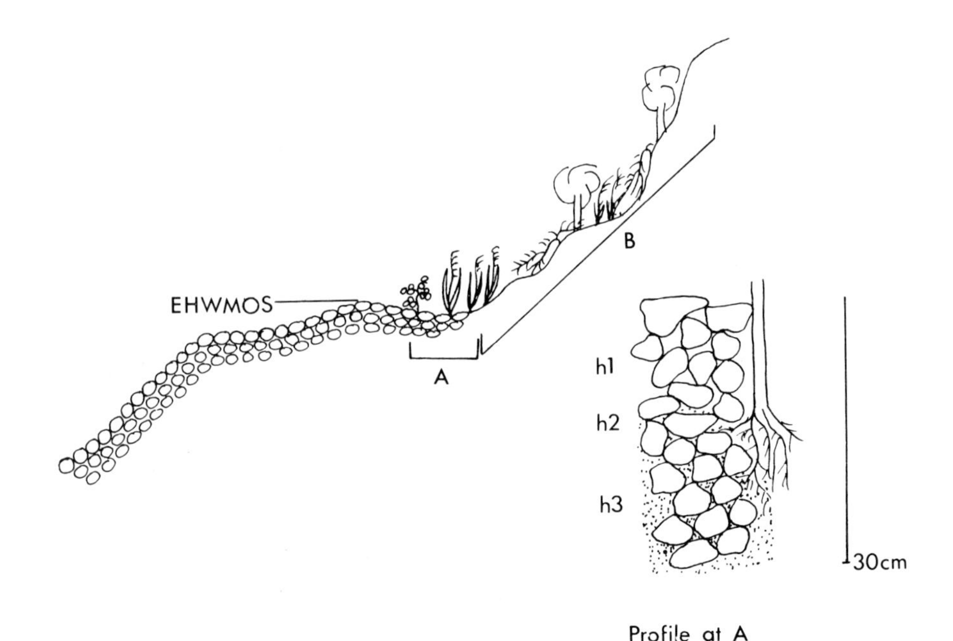

Figure 7 Diagrammatic profile of boulder beach

EROSION BANK

Where low-lying land gives way to a rocky shore, the soil and vegetation are often eroded to leave a low, steep slope to the foreshore, often only 1-3 m high. The erosion banks thus formed often have a distinct zonation of vegetation. The uppermost zone, C, can be grassland, woodland, scrub or any other typical land vegetation. Zone B is a strandline vegetation of such species as *Atriplex, Rumex* and *Sonchus*. The upper littoral zone A is usually devoid of vegetation.

Ligia oceanica was almost the only species to occur in zone A. In zone B, *Porcellio scaber, Armadillidium vulgare* and *Cylisticus convexus* were most frequently found under loose rocks or larger pieces of strandline debris. Smaller species occurred mainly under rocks lying on eroded soil and among the roots of strandline plants (h1): close to the surface, *Trichoniscus pusillus* and *Androniscus dentiger* were most frequent, but deeper down, under the larger stones and deep among roots, *Trichoniscus pygmaeus* and *Trichoniscoides saeroeensis* occurred. The same larger species occurred in zone C but, where large stones were embedded in the soil (h2), a greater variety of small soil-dwelling species was recorded, with *Haplophthalmus mengei* often the most frequent. This severely limited and fragile habitat was where *Metatrichoniscoides celticus* occurred in south Wales.

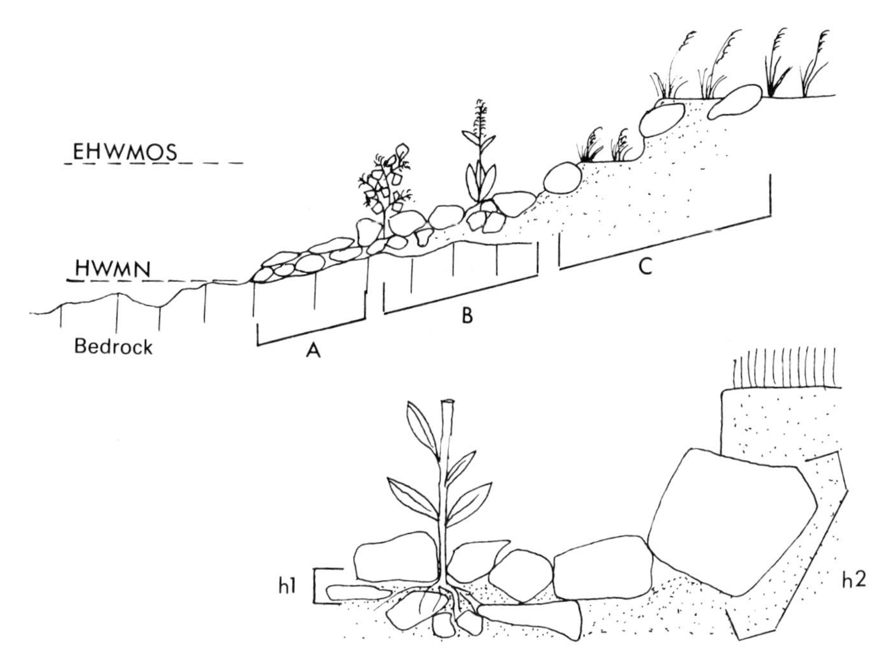

Figure 8 Diagrammatic profile of erosion bank

VEGETATED CLIFF

This basic habitat covers a wide variety of different types, depending on the underlying rock type, slope, aspect and exposure, and also the geographical area. The splash zone usually has a vegetation of lichens, scurvy-grass (*Cochlearia* spp.) and sea campion (*Silene maritima*), with further up the cliff, species such as rock samphire (*Crithmum maritimum*), greater sea-spurrey (*Spergularia media*), thrift (*Armeria maritima*), rock sea lavender (*Limonium binervosum*) and sea plantain (*Plantago maritima*). Transition into a dense grassy sward is often gradual and may, in fact, be into low scrub of scrambling shrubs (brambles, roses, etc) rather than grass. Where cliffs are grazed, the grassland is often short so that woodlice are unable to shelter in the grass litter and tend to occur in crevices, under stones and in the soil.

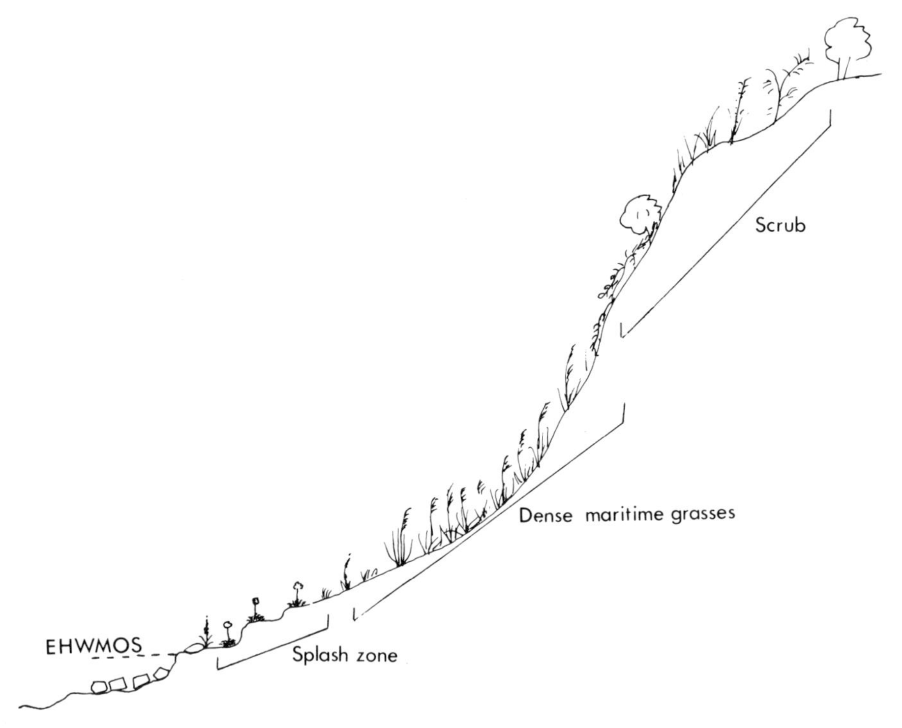

Figure 9 Diagrammatic profile of vegetated cliff

The fauna of the splash zone is very rich, with many soil-dwelling species occurring in the damp loamy soil derived from drift material and the litter of mat-forming species such as sea campion; *Androniscus dentiger, Haplophthalmus mengei, Trichoniscoides saeroeensis, Trichoniscus pusillus* and *Trichoniscus pygmaeus* have all been recorded. The foliage of mat-forming plants was found to provide day shelter sites for *Porcellionides cingendus* and *Eluma purpurascens*, as well as for the much commoner *Porcellio scaber* and *Armadillidium vulgare. Ligia oceanica*, and very rarely *Halophiloscia couchi*, also occurred in the splash zone.

Grassy swards further up the cliffs supported *A. vulgare, Philoscia muscorum, P. scaber* and, more rarely, *Armadillidium depressum, Armadillidium nasatum* and *Armadillidium pulchellum*. The last species was found in Wales and Scotland mainly under flat stones, often in association with ants. In such situations in the south, *Platyarthrus hoffmannseggi* was common.

The fauna of scrub on cliffs was similar to that of shaded situations inland, but species dependent on base-rich soils occurred in otherwise unexpected sites on acidic rocks, probably as a result of wind-borne sea spray maintaining more basic soil conditions.

Three species merit special mention. *Androniscus dentiger* and *Cylisticus convexus* seem to be especially common in association with seepages on cliffs, particularly those cliffs composed of clay or other soft rocks. These species were most frequently encountered on the cliff face during darkness. *Miktoniscus patiencei* was recorded in deep, friable soil under dense fescue (*Festuca*) grassland, usually in sheltered clefts in the cliff face, only a metre or two above the rocky shore edge where only lichens grow.

STEEP SOIL-LESS CLIFF

Steep cliffs which lack soil and vegetation appear to be inhabited by few species of woodlice. Throughout the British Isles, *Ligia oceanica* was common on such cliffs wherever sampled. On exposed southern and western coasts, *Halophiloscia couchi* was found, but its nocturnal habits and the inaccessibility of its day shelter sites often made this species difficult to find (Harding 1973, 1975).

More species were encountered where a boulder talus had formed at the base of the cliff, especially if drift material had decayed to form soil among the talus. The fauna was the same as that described for erosion banks.

On very exposed cliffs, the effects of maritime influences were seen, often as much as 100 m above high water mark; *Ligia oceanica* was found at the top of several high cliffs, and *Trichoniscoides saeroeensis* was found among the roots of vegetation, or beneath deeply embedded stones, on cliff tops.

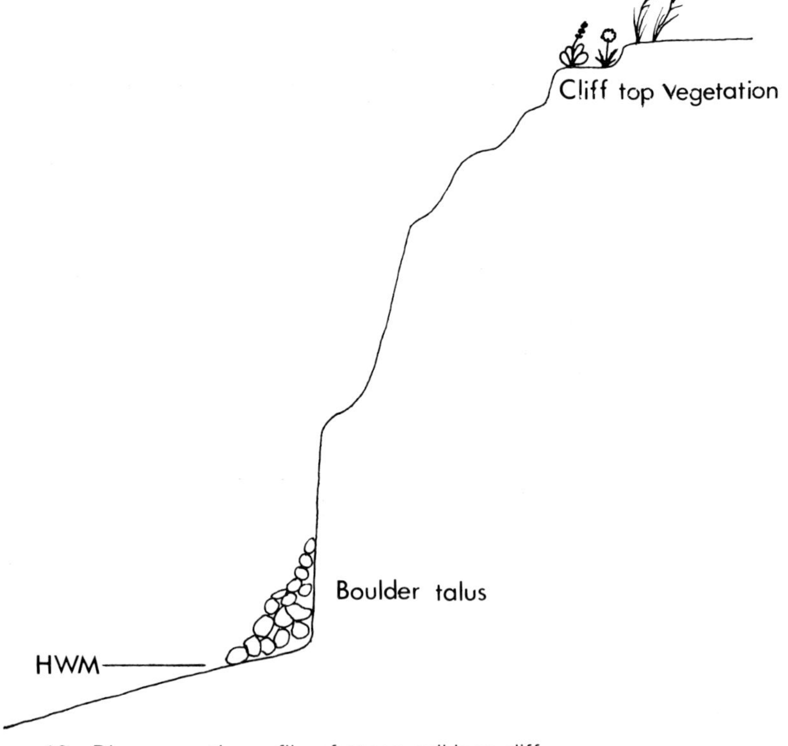

Figure 10 Diagrammatic profile of steep soil-less cliff

2nd Order Habitats

Table 4 *2nd Order Habitats:* Percentage of records for each species in selected habitats

	Number of records	Number of species recorded	Androniscus dentiger	Armadillidium depressum	A. nasatum	A. pictum	A. pulchellum	A. vulgare	Cylisticus convexus	Eluma purpurascens	Halophiloscia couchi	Haplophthalmus danicus	H. mengei	Ligia oceanica	Ligidium hypnorum	Metatrichoniscoides celticus
Hedge	628	16	0.32	0.32				8.12		0.16		0.95	0.64			
Roadside verge	2493	24	1.49	0.04	0.28	0.04	0.04	9.95	0.04			1.12	0.72	0.08	0.20	
Embankment/cutting	812	20	2.96	0.25	0.62		0.37	9.86	0.25	0.25			1.48	0.25	0.37	
Dry stone wall	663	16	0.45	0.45		0.15	0.45	5.58					0.15	0.60		
Wall with mortar	987	16	3.65	2.13	0.41			7.30	0.81		0.10		0.51	1.52		
Quarry (face and floor)	883	20	4.16	1.18	1.49			11.30	0.37	0.06		0.31	2.91		0.06	
Natural cliff face	887	22	2.59	0.45	0.34		1.35	12.29	0.79	1.47	0.56		1.92	5.98		0.11
Screes	692	23	4.52	0.76	1.41	0.28	3.76	8.01	2.18		0.57	0.09	2.82	1.61		0.57
Road/path	515	19	6.41	0.78	0.78			8.35	0.78			0.58	0.58	0.19	0.19	

	Miktoniscus patiencei	Oniscus asellus	Oritoniscus flavus	Philoscia muscorum	Platyarthrus hoffmannseggi	Porcellio dilatatus	P. laevis	P. scaber	P. spinicornis	Porcellionides cingendus	P. pruinosus	Trachelipus rathkei	Trichoniscoides albidus	T. saeroeensis	T. sarsi	Trichoniscus pusillus	T. pygmaeus
Hedge		28.19	0.16	20.70	0.95			23.25		0.80	0.95	0.16				12.10	2.23
Roadside verge		25.60	0.12	18.06	1.77	0.08		19.02	0.20	1.12	0.20	0.12	0.04		0.04	16.90	2.41
Embankment/cutting		24.04		16.52	3.95			14.06	0.37	2.34	0.12	0.61	0.12			18.62	2.71
Dry stone wall		27.60	0.15	10.56	1.81			27.45	9.50	2.72	0.45					10.26	1.66
Wall with mortar		25.33	0.30	9.73	1.72			22.70	13.58	0.81	0.41					8.11	0.81
Quarry (face and floor)		21.11	0.12	14.22	2.54			17.30	3.65	1.42	0.99	0.12				13.03	3.66
Natural cliff face	0.34	19.62	0.11	13.08	1.92			20.74	0.23	4.74				0.56		8.79	2.03
Screes		23.13		9.39	1.79	0.09		14.69	1.60	0.94				0.28	0.28	17.56	3.66
Road/path		22.91		12.04	2.33		0.19	20.97	2.91	1.94	0.97					14.56	2.52

(NB *Armadillidium album, Buddelundiella cataractae* and *Stenophiloscia zosterae* were not recorded in any of these habitats.)

GLOSSARY

The following is not intended to be a comprehensive glossary of terms used in this volume but rather to explain a few possibly unfamiliar words.

Chromatophores Cells in which the distribution of colour pigment can be contracted or expanded, allowing the animal to change its colour or pattern.

Endopod The inner branch of the crustacean limb. In woodlice, only the limbs of the pleon retain the primitive branched state. The endopods are flattened plates on the ventral surface except for the last pair which form the inner branch of the uropods.

Epimera The projecting lateral edges of the dorsal plates (pereonites) of the body.

Eskers Ridges of gravel and sand formed by streams flowing in the ice of an ice-sheet or glacier and which were left when the ice melted.

Eurytopic Tolerant of a wide range of habitats.

Exopod The outer branch of the crustacean limb (see *Endopod*). The last pair form the outer branch of the uropods.

Gonochoristic Male and female individuals in the same population (roughly 50:50 ratio implied).

Haplophthalmoid Having the characteristics of the genus *Haplophthalmus*.

Microsite As used in the Isopod Survey Scheme, the exact site where an animal was found (cf microhabitat—the place where an animal is usually found).

Pereon The middle section of the body; of 7 segments, each with a pair of walking limbs.

Pereonites The dorsal plates of the pereon, one per segment.

Pleon The rear section of the body. It is much shorter than the pereon and ends in the telson. The limbs are flattened plates modified for respiration (and further modified for sperm transfer in the male).

Pleonites The dorsal plates of the pleon.

Pleopodal lungs Formerly usually called *pseudotracheae*, these are air-filled tubes ramifying through the interior of the pleopod exopods. They are bathed in blood and have a respiratory function. We follow Holdich *et al.* (1984) in calling them pleopodal lungs.

Scutellum The central dorsal ridge forming the 'forehead' of woodlice, particularly noticeable as a distinctive 'snout' (*A. nasatum*).

Synanthropic Living in association with man.

Talus Rock debris at the base of a cliff.

Telson The posterior projection of the pleon. It is often pointed, but may be rounded or quadrangular.

Tergite A dorsal plate (sclerite) of the cuticle. Hence *tergal.*

Tullgren funnel An apparatus for extracting arthropods from soil and leaf litter. It consists of a source of light and heat (commonly a 60 W bulb) and a funnel. The soil/litter is supported on a mesh at the widest part of the funnel and emerging animals fall into preservative below.

Uropods The much modified last pair of pleopods, with 2 branches each side flanking the telson.

Xerophilic Thriving in dry habitats.

REFERENCES

Al-Dabbagh, K. Y. & Block, W. 1981. Population ecology of a terrestrial isopod in two Breckland grass heaths. *J. Anim. Ecol.*, **50,** 61–77.

Barrett, K. E. J. 1979. *Provisional atlas of the insects of the British Isles. Part 5. Hymenoptera: Formicidae (Ants).* Abbots Ripton: Institute of Terrestrial Ecology.

Bate, C. S. & Westwood, J. O. 1868. *A history of the British sessile-eyed Crustacea, vol. 2.* London: Van Voorst.

Bolton, B. & Collingwood, C. A. 1975. *Hymenoptera: Formicidae.* (Handbooks for the identification of British insects **6,** 3(c).) London: Royal Entomological Society of London.

Bowman, T. E. & Abele, L. G. 1982. Classification of the recent Crustacea. In: *The biology of Crustacea,* edited by L. G. Abele, **1,** 1–27. London: Academic Press.

Brooks, J. L. 1942. Notes on the ecology and the occurrence in America of the myrmecophilous sowbug, *Platyarthrus hoffmannseggi* Brandt. *Ecology,* **23,** 427–437.

Caruso, D. & Brisolese, S. 1974. Ricerche bioecologiche sulla fauna delle grotte vulcaniche dell'Etna. *Animalia Catania,* **1,** 123–133.

Clapham, A. R., Tutin, T. G. & Warburg E. F. 1981. *Excursion flora of the British Isles.* 3rd ed. Cambridge: Cambridge University Press.

Collinge, W. E. 1917. Note on an apparently rare British woodlouse (*Ligidium hypnorum,* Cuv.). *Scott. Nat.,* **63,** 94–95.

Collinge, W. E. 1918a. *Porcellio rathkei*—a woodlouse new to the Irish fauna. *Ir. Nat.,* **27,** 1–2.

Collinge, W. E. 1918b. Some remarks upon the terrestrial isopod, *Porcellio ratzeburgii* Brandt. *J. zool. Res.,* **3,** 103–105.

Collinge, W. E. 1942a. On the distribution of *Philoscia couchi* Kinahan in Great Britain. *NWest. Nat.,* **17,** 10.

Collinge, W. E. 1942b. On a new variety of *Haplophthalmus danicus*. *NWest. Nat.,* **17,** 11.

Collinge, W. E. 1943a. *Porcellio ratzeburgii* Brandt: its distribution in Great Britain. *NWest. Nat.,* **18,** 14.

Collinge, W. E. 1943b. The distribution in Great Britain of the genus *Trichoniscoides* Sars. *NWest. Nat.,* **18,** 267–268.

Collinge, W. E. 1944a. The distribution in Great Britain of three species of the genus *Porcellio*. *NWest. Nat.,* **19,** 235–237.

Collinge, W. E. 1944b. On two terrestrial Isopoda new to the Irish fauna. *Ann. Mag. nat. Hist., Ser. 11,* **11,** 207–208.

Collinge, W. E. 1944c. The distribution in Great Britain of the genus *Armadillidium* Brandt. *NWest. Nat.,* **19,** 119–122.

Cotton, M. J. 1967. Aspects of the ecology of sand-dune arthropods. *Entomologist,* **100,** 157–165.

Crowson, R. A. & Crowson E. A. 1963. Observations on insects and arachnids from the Scottish south coast. *Glasg. Nat.,* **18,** 228–232.

Cummings, B. F 1907. Notes on terrestrial isopods from north Devon. *Zoologist,* **11,** 465–470.

Dandy, J. E. 1969. *Watsonian vice-counties of Great Britain.* London: Ray Society.

Davis, B. N. K. & Jones, P. E. 1978. The ground arthropods of some chalk and limestone quarries in England. *J. Biogeogr.,* **5,** 159–171.

Davis, R. C. 1984. Effects of weather and habitat structure on the population dynamics of three species of woodlice (Crustacea: Oniscoidea) in dune grassland. *Oikos,* **42,** 387–395.

Davis,R. C. & Sutton, S. L. 1978. A comparative study of changes in biomass of isopods inhabiting dune grassland. *Sci. Proc. R. Dublin Soc., Ser. A,* **6,** 223–233.

Davis, R. C., Hassall, M. & Sutton, S. L. 1977. The vertical distribution of isopods and diplopods in a dune grassland. *Pedobiologia,* **17,** 320–329.

Dexter, R. W. 1959. Records of the sea-side isopod *Ligia oceanica* at Cape Ann, Massachusetts. *Ecology,* **40,** 507.

Dexter, R. W. 1972. Additional records of the sea-side isopod *Ligia oceanica* at Cape Ann, Massachusetts, USA. *Crustaceana,* Suppl. no. 3, 100.

Dominiak, B. 1961. Badania nad Rownonogami (Isopoda, Crustacea) z Rodzaju *Haplophthalmus* schobl. W. Polsce. *Badan. fizjogr. Pol. zachod.,* **8,** 7–22.

Donisthorpe, H. StJ. K. 1927. *The guests of British ants, their habits and life-histories.* London: Routledge.

Doogue, D. & Harding, P. T. 1982. *Distribution atlas of woodlice in Ireland.* Dublin: An Foras Forbartha.

Edney, E. B. 1953. The woodlice of Great Britain and Ireland—a concise systematic monograph. *Proc. Linn. Soc. Lond.,* **164,** 49–98.

Edney, E. B. 1954. *British woodlice.* (Synopses of the British fauna, no. 9.) London: Linnean Society.

Ellis, A. E. 1943. Notes on the woodlice of Surrey. *Proc. Trans. Croydon nat. Hist. scient. Soc.,* **11,** 152–153.

Ellis, J. P. & Lincoln, R. J. 1975. Catalogue of the types of terrestrial isopods (Oniscoidea) in the collections of the British Museum (Natural History), II. Oniscoidea, excluding Pseudotracheata. *Bull. Br. Mus. nat. Hist., Ser. D. Zool.,* **28,** 65–100.

Evans, W. 1900. *Platyarthrus hoffmannseggi* Brandt, in Fife. *Ann. Scot. nat. Hist.,* **35,** 186.

Fairhurst, C. P., Barber, A. D. & Armitage, M. L. 1978. The British Myriapod Survey—April 1975. *Abh. Verh. naturw. Ver. Hamburg,* NS, **21/22,** 129–134.

Frankel, B. 1973. Distinguishing male secondary markings on two sub-species of the woodlouse *Trichoniscus pusillus* Brandt. *Entomologist's mon. Mag.,* **109,** 109.

Frankel, B. 1976. *The taxonomic status, biology and ecology of the woodlouse* Trichoniscus pusillus *Brandt 1833 in Epping Forest.* PhD thesis, University of London.

Frankel, B. 1979a. The juvenile stadia of the diploid and triploid subspecies of *Trichoniscus pusillus* Brandt (Crustacea: Isopoda). *Jnl nat. Hist.,* **13,** 195–210.

Frankel, B. 1979b. Comparative growth patterns of the diploid and triploid subspecies of Trichoniscus pusillus (Crustacea, Isopoda). *Pedobiologia,* **19,** 293–308.

Frankel, B., Sutton, S. L. & Fussey, G. D. 1981. The sex ratios of *Trichoniscus pusillus* Brandt (Crustacea: Oniscoidea). *Jnl nat. Hist.,* **15,** 301–307.

Fussey, G. D. 1984. The distribution of the two forms of the woodlouse *Trichoniscus pusillus* Brandt (Isopoda: Oniscoidea) in the British Isles: a reassessment of geographic parthenogenesis. *Biol. J. Linnean Soc. Lond.,* **23,** 309–321.

Fussey, G. D. & Sutton, S. L. 1981. The identification and distribution of the bisexual and parthenogenetic forms of *Trichoniscus pusillus* (Isopoda: Oniscoidea) in Ireland. *Ir. Nat. J.,* **20,** 196–199.

Girling, M. 1979. Calcium carbonate replaced arthropods from archaeological deposits. *J. archaeol. Sci.,* **6,** 309–320.

Gorvett, H. & Taylor, J. C. 1960. A further note on tegumental glands in woodlice. *Proc. zool. Soc. Lond.,* **133,** 653–655.

Gruner, H. E. 1966. *Die Tierwelt Deutschlands: Krebstiere oder Crustacea. 5: Isopoda,* vol. 2. Jena: Fischer.

Harding, P. T. 1968a. Notes on the biology and distribution of *Armadillidium album* Dollfus (Crustacea: Isopoda, Oniscoidea) in the British Isles. *Entomologist's mon. Mag.*, **104,** 269–272.

Harding, P. T. 1968b. A list of woodlice (Crustacea: Isopoda: Oniscoidea) from the Burren, Co. Clare. *Ir. Nat. J.*, **16,** 16–17.

Harding, P. T. 1969. Further records of *Armadillidium album* Dollfus (Crustacea: Isopoda: Oniscoidea) from Ireland, and other notes and records. *Ir. Nat. J.*, **16,** 166–167.

Harding, P. T. 1971. Notes on the occurrence of woodlice (Isopoda: Oniscoidea) on sand-dunes at Whiteford Burrows, Glamorgan. *Entomologist,* **104,** 98–103.

Harding, P. T. 1973. *The occurrence of the littoral woodlouse* Halophiloscia couchi *(Kinahan) in the British Isles.* Unpublished report on Project 20/73 (P) to the World Wildlife Fund (British National Appeal).

Harding, P. T. 1975. Observations on the habitat of *Halophiloscia couchi* (Kinahan 1858) (Isopoda, Oniscoidea) in southwestern Britain. *Crustaceana,* **28,** 108–109.

Harding, P. T. ed. 1976a. *Provisional atlas of the Crustacea of the British Isles, part 1. Isopoda: Oniscoidea, Woodlice.* Abbots Ripton: Institute of Terrestrial Ecology.

Harding, P. T. 1976b. *Eluma purpurascens* Budde-Lund (Crustacea: Isopoda) a woodlouse new to Britain from Norfolk. *Trans. Norfolk Norwich Nat. Soc.*, **23,** 267–268.

Harding, P. T. 1977. A re-examination of the work of W. E. Collinge on woodlice (Crustacea, Isopoda, Oniscoidea) from the British Isles. *J. Soc. Bibliogr. nat. Hist.*, **8,** 286–315.

Harding, P. T. 1982. An annotated list of Huntingdonshire woodlice (Isopoda: Oniscoidea). *Rep. Huntingdon. Fauna Flora Soc., 1981,* no. 34, 18–20.

Harding, P. T. (In preparation) *A bibliography of the distribution and ecology of woodlice in Great Britain.*

Harding, P. T., Collis, G. M. & Collis, V. D. 1979. The pill woodlouse (*Armadillidium vulgare* (Latr.)) (Isopoda) in Scotland. *Entomologist's mon. Mag.*, **115,** 179–180.

Harding, P. T., Cotton, M. J. & Rundle, A. J. 1980. The occurrence of *Halophiloscia (Stenophiloscia) zosterae* Verhoeff, 1928 (Isopoda: Oniscoidea) in Britain. *Crustaceana,* **39,** 111–112.

Hassall, M. & Sutton, S. L. 1978. The role of isopods as decomposers in a dune grassland ecosystem. *Sci. Proc. R. Dublin Soc., Ser. A,* **6,** 235–245.

Healey, V. 1963. *Studies on the ecology of the woodlouse* Trichoniscus pusillus pusillus *Brandt 1833.* PhD. thesis, University of Manchester.

Holdich, D. M. & Lincoln, R. J. 1974. The distribution and habitat preferences of British marine isopods: a survey scheme. *Fld Stud.*, **4,** 97–104.

Holdich, D. M., Lincoln, R. J. & Ellis, J. P. 1984. The biology of terrestrial isopods: terminology and classificiation. In: *The biology of terrestrial isopods,* edited by S. L. Sutton & D. M. Holdich. (Symposium of the Zoological Society of London no. 53). Oxford: Clarendon.

Holthuis, L. B. 1947. On a small collection of isopod Crustacea from the greenhouses of the Royal Botanic Gardens, Kew. *Ann. Mag. nat. Hist., Ser. 11,* **13,** 122–137.

Howard, H. W. 1981. Constancy of polymorphism in three populations of the terrestrial isopod, *Armadillidium vulgare. Heredity, Lond.*, **47,** 135–137.

Ing B. 1959. Woodlice in Cambridgeshire. *Nature Cambs.*, **2,** 16–20.

Kinahan, J. R. 1857. Analysis of certain allied genera of terrestrial Isopoda. *Nat. Hist. Rev.*, **4,** 258–282.

Kinahan, J. R. 1858. On the genera *Philoscia* Latr., *Itea* Koch, *Philougria* Kinahan, comprising descriptions of new British species. *Nat. Hist. Rev.*, **5,** 194–200.

Lawlor, L. R. 1976a. Parental investment and offspring fitness in the terrestrial isopod *Armadillidium vulgare* (Latr.) (Crustacea: Oniscoidea). *Evolution, Lancaster, Pa,* **30,** 775–785.

Lawlor, L. R. 1976b. Molting, growth and reproductive strategies in the terrestrial isopod *Armadillidium vulgare. Ecology,* **57,** 1179–1194.

Legrand, J. J. 1942. Les Isopodes terrestres des environs de Paris. I. Description de quelques formes nouvelles. *Bull. Soc. zool. Fr.,* **67,** 153–161.

Legrand, J. J. 1949. Contribution à l'étude des Isopodes terrestres de la Bretagne. *Bull. Soc. zool. Fr.,* **74,** 53–67.

Legrand, J. J., Strouhal, H. & Vandel, A. 1950. Remarques critiques sur quelques Trichoniscidae (Isopodes terrestres). *Bull. Soc. zool. Fr.,* **75,** 307–312.

Lloyd, M. 1963. Numerical observations on movements of animals between beech litter and fallen branches. *J. Anim. Ecol.,* **32,** 157–163.

McQueen, D. G. 1976. The influence of climatic factors on the demography of the terrestrial isopod *Tracheoniscus rathkei* Brandt. *Can. J. Zool.,* **54,** 2185–2199.

Meinertz, T. 1950. The distribution of the terrestrial isopods in Denmark and some remarks on their distribution in neighbouring countries. *Vidensk. Meddr. dansk naturh. Foren.,* **112,** 165–223.

Moon, H. P. & Harding, P. T. 1981. *A preliminary review of the occurrence of* Asellus *(Crustacea: Isopoda) in the British Isles.* Abbots Ripton: Institute of Terrestrial Ecology. (Unpublished).

Norman, A. M. 1899. British land Isopoda. *Ann. Mag. nat. Hist., Ser. 7,* **3,** 70–78.

Norman, A. M. 1903. British land Isopoda—Supplement. *Ann. Mag. nat. Hist., Ser. 7,* **11,** 369–372.

O'Connor, J. 1945. Annual migration of slaters on the Fastnet Rock, Co. Mayo. *Ir. Nat. J.,* **8,** 268–269.

Oliver, P. G. 1983. The occurrence of *Buddelundiella cataractae* Verhoeff, 1930 (Isopoda: Oniscoidea) in Wales, Great Britain. *Crustaceana,* **44,** 105–108.

Oliver, P. G. & Sutton, S. L. 1982. *Miktoniscus patiencei* Vandel, 1946. (Isopoda: Oniscoidea), a redescription with notes on its occurrence in Britain and Eire. *Jnl nat. Hist.,* **16,** 201–208.

Oliver, P. G. & Trew, A. 1981. A new species of *Metatrichoniscoides* (Isopoda: Oniscoidea) from the coast of South Wales, UK. *Jnl nat. Hist.,* **15,** 525–529.

Pack Beresford, D. R. 1908. *Eluma purpurascens*—a woodlouse new to the British Isles. *Ir. Nat.,* **17,** 255–258.

Pack Beresford, D. R. & Foster, N. H. 1911. The woodlice of Ireland: their distribution and classification. *Proc. R. Ir. Acad. B.,* **29,** 165–190.

Palmén, E. 1947. Zur Kenntnis der Trichonisciden (Isopoda terr.) Finnlands. *Ann. zool. Soc. zool. bot. fenn. Vanamo,* **13,** 1–22.

Paris, O. H. 1963. The ecology of *Armadillidium vulgare* (Isopoda: Oniscoidea) in California grassland: food, enemies and weather. *Ecol. Mon.,* **33,** 1–22.

Parry, G. 1953. Osmotic and ionic regulation in the isopod crustacean *Ligia oceanica. J. exp. Biol.,* **30,** 567–574.

Percival, E. 1929. A report on the fauna of the estuaries of the River Tamar and the River Lynher. *J. mar. biol. Ass. U.K.,* **16,** 81–108.

Phillipson, J. 1983. Life cycle, number, biomass and respiratory metabolism of *Trichoniscus pusillus* (Crustacea: Isopoda) in a beech woodland—Wytham Woods, Oxford. *Oecologia,* **57,** 339–342.

Scannell, M. J. P. & Synnott, D. M. 1972. *Census catalogue of the flora of Ireland.* Dublin: Stationery Office.

Scharff, R. F 1894. The Irish woodlice (with descriptions and figures of all the British species). *Ir. Nat.*, **3,** 4–7, 25–29.

Schultz, G. A. 1961. Distribution and establishment of a land isopod in North America. *Syst. Zool.*, **10,** 193–196.

Sheppard, E. M. 1968. *Trichoniscoides saeroeensis* Lohmander, an isopod new to the British fauna. *Trans. Cave Res. Grp Gt Br.*, **10,** 135–137.

Shirt, D. B. ed. 1985. *British red data books: 2. Insects.* Peterborough: Nature Conservancy Council. In press.

Standen, R. 1913. *Armadillidium pictum* Brandt in Westmorland: a species new to the British Isles. *Lancs. Nat.*, **6,** 121–122.

Standen, R. 1922. *Ligidium hypnorum* Cuvier in Lancashire. *Lancs. Chesh. Nat.*, **14,** 215–216.

Standen, V. 1970. The life history of *Trichoniscus pusillus pusillus* (Crustacea: Isopoda). *J. Zool.*, **161,** 461–470.

Standen, V. 1973. The life cycle and annual production of *Trichoniscus pusillus pusillus* (Crustacea: Isopoda) in a Cheshire wood. *Pedobiologia*, **13,** 273–291.

Stebbing, T. R. R. 1873. On a crustacean of the genus *Zia. Ann. Mag. nat. Hist., Ser. 4,* **11,** 286–288.

Sunderland, K. D. & Sutton, S. L. 1980. A serological study of predation on terrestrial isopods in a dune grassland ecosystem. *J. Anim. Ecol.*, **49,** 987–1004.

Sunderland, K. D., Hassall, M. & Sutton, S. L. 1976. The population dynamics of *Philoscia muscorum* (Crustacea: Oniscoidea) in a dune grassland ecosystem. *J. Anim. Ecol.*, **45,** 487–506.

Sutton, S. L. 1966. *The ecology of isopod populations in grassland.* D.Phil. thesis, University of Oxford.

Sutton, S. L. 1968. The population dynamics of *Trichoniscus pusillus* and *Philoscia muscorum* (Crustacea: Oniscoidea) in limestone grassland. *J. Anim. Ecol.*, **37,** 425–444.

Sutton, S. L. 1970. Growth patterns in *Trichoniscus pusillus* and *Philoscia muscorum* (Crustacea: Oniscoidea). *Pedobiologia*, **10,** 434–441.

Sutton, S. L. 1972. *Woodlice.* London: Ginn.

Sutton S. L. 1980. *Woodlice.* Oxford: Pergamon Press.

Sutton, S. L. & Coghill, H. 1979. Woodlice and their control. *Leafl. Minist. Agric. Fish. Fd,* no. 623.

Sutton S. L. & Holdich D. M. eds. 1984. *The biology of terrestrial isopods.* (Symposium of the Zoological Society of London no. 53). Oxford: Clarendon.

Sutton, S. L., Harding, P. T. & Burn, D. 1972. *Key to British woodlice.* London: Ginn.

Sutton, S. L., Hassall, M., Willows, R., Davis, R. C., Grundy, A. & Sunderland, K. D. 1984. Life histories of terrestrial isopods: a study of intra- and interspecific variation. In: *The biology of terrestrial isopods,* edited by S. L. Sutton & D. M. Holdich. (Symposium of the Zoological Society of London no. 53). Oxford: Clarendon.

Swan, E. F 1956. Isopods of the genus *Ligia* on the New England coast. *Ecology,* **37,** 204–206.

Taylor, E. 1932. On *Porcellio ratzeburgii* Brandt and its occurrence in Lancashire and Cheshire. *NWest. Nat.*, **7,** 117–118.

Taylor, E. 1936. Report on Oniscoidea (Woodlice). *Proc. Rep. Ashmol. nat. Hist. Soc. Oxf.*, 1935, 16–17.

Taylor, E. 1938. The Crustacea of Suffolk: Part II. Oniscoidea or woodlice. *Trans. Suffolk Nat. Soc.*, **4,** 28–30.

Templeton, R. 1836. Catalogue of the Irish Crustacea, Myriapoda and Arachnoida, selected from the papers of the late John Templeton Esq. *Mag. nat. Hist.*, **9,** 9–14.

Vandel, A. 1960a. *Isopodes terrestres* (Première Partie). (Faune de France no. 64). Paris: Lechevalier.

Vandel, A. 1960b. Les Isopodes terrestres de l'Archipel Madérien. *Mém. Mus. natn. Hist. nat., Paris, A. Zoologie,* **22,** 1–156.

Vandel, A. 1962. *Isopodes terrestres.* (Deuxième partie). (Faune de France no. 66). Paris: Lechevalier.

Webb, D. A. 1980. The biological vice-counties of Ireland. *Proc. R. Ir. Acad., B,* **80,** 179–196.

Webb, W. M. 1899. The occurrence in Essex of a species of woodlouse (Isopoda) new to Britain (*Porcellio ratzeburgi* Brandt). *Essex Nat.,* **11,** 127.

Webb, W. M. & Sillem, C. 1906. *The British woodlice.* London: Duckworth.

Wells, S. M., Pyle, R. M. & Collins, N. M. 1983. *The IUCN invertebrate red data book.* Gland: IUCN.

APPENDIX 1

LIST OF RECORDERS

The following list includes the 436 recorders who contributed records during the course of the survey. It does not include the collectors of material in museums, collected before the survey began, or recorders who provided only records of *Asellus* species.

We are very grateful to everyone listed below for their contribution to the survey; without them, little would have been achieved.

Addey J E
Aitken P
Al-Dabbagh K Y
Alexander K N A
Anderson R
Angus S
Arnold G A
Arnold H R
Asker M
Axford S
Bailey S
Ball J
Barber A D
Barbour T F
Barnes R M
Barrett B W
Bell A A
Bevan A M
Bishop J D
Bishop M H
Block W R
Blower J G
Bolton D
Boot K
Bray R P
Briggs C F
Brinklow R K
Britt D P
Brown B
Browne P
Bryant C
Buchan P B
Buckley P
Bull S
Bullard E
Burgess F
Burns P F
Burton P A
Burton R G
Butler P M
Calder C
Cameron R A D
Campbell J L
Campbell L
Carr H
Carr J W
Chater A O
Chatfield J E
Cheke R
Chrichton M
Christie L
Clarke A S
Clarkson K
Clements H A B
Colebourn P H
Collins D R
Collis G M and V D
Cooke J A L
Cooter J
Copson P J
Corlett H
Cotton D C F
Cotton M J
Cowham N
Cranbrook, Earl of
Crawford A K
Crawley C
Crawshaw D I
Credland P G
Cremona J
Crisp D T
Crocker J
Croot G E
Crosby T S
Crowson R A
Cuffy F
Dalton D F
Daniel R and students
Darlington J P E C
Daulman M
Davey S
Davies L
Davis A
Davis B N K
Davis R C
Dawson N
Denton M
Dickinson J A
Dixon J
Dixon R
Dolling M
Dony J G
Doogue D
Dooley M
Driscoll R J
Duffey E
Dure-Smith M
Edney E B
Edwards A C
Edwards T
Eeles J
Elliott M M
Ellis E A
Elton C S
Ely W A
Evans L
Evans M S
Evans P
Eyeons E
Eyres M
Fairhurst C P and J

Farrell L
Felton C
Finegan R P
Fleming S
Flint G
Fogan M
Fowler S V
Fox P
Fox P J
Frank H
Frankel B
Frazer O H
Freestone S and P
Fussey G D
Garland S P
Garrad L
Gauld I D
Gaze R
George D
George R S
Gibson L
Gilbert J L
Goddard D G
Goldsmith J G
Good A C
Good J
Goodall A and M
Grace K
Gray J R A
Greatbanks C
Greatorex-Davies J N
Green B
Guntrip D
Hadley M
Hancock E G
Hand S C
Hanson D
Harding C M
Harding P M
Harding P T
Harper R J
Harris J I
Harris J M
Hart A
Hassall M
Hazelton M
Henderson T W
Hennelly M
Hennessy M
Herringshaw D
Higgins D
Hinxman A
Hodges M
Holden E
Holdich D M
Holland D G
Holmes A
Hounsome M V
Howard H W
Hoyle J A
Hudson G
Hughes A L
Humphries D
Hunter M
Huxley M
Huxley T
Hyatt K H
Ing B
Ingle R W
Irwin A G
Jackson N C S
Jackson R
Jagoe R B
Jefferies K and D J
Johnson C
Jones P E
Jones R E
Judson G A
Kearns H
Keay A
Kendall P
Kennedy R J
Kerr D
Keys J
Khaloyan O K
Kidd L N
Kiernan D
King G J
Knight N
Landworthy V
Lass R A
Lawrence P N
LePage D M
Lee E
Leeming J P
Lees D
Levinge D
Lewenz P
Lincoln R J
Lindley M E
Line J M
Lloyd-Evans L
Lockwood A P H
Long G
Loxton R G
Loynds G A
Loze K R
Luff M L
Lynch D
MacDonald M
MacFarlane D
Macfadyen F A
Mackay D W
Mackie C
Mackie D W
Maclean N
Maloney C
Mander P B
Manning S A
Mantle R J
Marsh D
Mason E C
Mason R
Matthams R
Maughan E
Maxwell W G R
McAllister R I
McCutcheon D E
McDonald P W
McDonald R
McGrath D
McGuirk
McMillan N F
McNae G
McNahan D
Mendel H
Messent R K
Messer D
Messer L
Metcalfe R J A
Middleton D
Miles P M
Mill P J
Mitchell D W
Mitchell G D
Mitchell H
Moller G J
Montgomery R
Moon H P
Moore J W
Morgan H G
Moriarty C
Morris M G

Morton A
Moseley C M
Mothersill C
Mounsey J D
Muchmore W B
Murie J A
Murphy C M
Murray D E
Murray W
Murrell S G
Mylroie A E
Naden J
Nash D A
Nash J A
Nattrass N P
Nau B S
Neill C
Newbold C
Newman N A
Newrich J N
Norris A
O'Connor J P
O'Donnell N
O'Mahoney P
O'Meara M
O'Neill M
O'Rourke F J
Oliver P G
Ord J
Osborn A G H
Osley N J
Overton H
Parfitt E
Parker H
Parmenter F R
Parr M J
Paul C R C
Payne K A
Pearce E J
Pearson V
Perry R
Philip D
Philp B
Philp E G
Picken G B
Pitts C
Plant C W
Plant R A
Pollard N
Poole S
Post R J
Pottinger E
Powell R P
Preston C D
Pritchard A
Pullen A
Quirk A
Randle B J
Rands E B
Rapp W F
Reardon N M
Reavell P E
Redmond M
Redshaw E J
Rees C J
Reeves P
Reynolds C
Reynolds L
Reynolds P
Rhodes P S
Rice A L
Richardson D T
Riley T H
Rob C M
Rodgers A
Rogers S
Roper J W
Rose A M
Rothwell D
Rundle A J
Sage J R
Sampson C P
Sander J I
Sanderson J M
Sawtell J
Scotter C
Seaward D R
Sharkey G
Sharpe D
Sharrock J T R
Shaw K
Sheppard E M
Shortt A
Shotton M F
Side K C
Singer E
Skelton M J L
Skidmore P
Smart J A
Smith C J
Smith J K
Smith M
Smith S J
Sommerville A
Southward E C
Spalding D A E
Spenser G G
Spooner G M
Staddon B W
Standen V
Stebbings R E
Stevens I H
Stewart P
Stott W G R and N
Strachan P W
Stroud D A
Sunderland K D
Sutton S L
Syvret K E
Taylor E
Teagle W G
Tew G S
Thomas J A
Thomas T J
Thomas W B
Thompson D
Tickle J A
Tinning P C
Topley P
Tortolano N
Towns M
Trew A
Tucker J H
Turner M A
Turner S
Tweedie M F W
Tyers I G
Usher M B
Varndell I
Wade P M
Wake P K
Walden H
Waley J
Wallace I D
Wallis P
Walpole M
Walters M G
Warburton S
Ward A L
Ward L K
Warren D M E
Waterston A R
Watson R

Watson R G
Watts C H S
Webster I
Welch R C
Wellard
Wells T C E
Westwood W D
White A J
White M G
Whitehead H
Williams G
Williamson E A
Williamson J
Willows R I
Wills H J
Wilson J
Wood R
Woolger A
Wright R

APPENDIX 2

SPECIES NEW TO THE BRITISH ISLES

(P G Oliver, National Museum of Wales)

The most recent revision of the British Isles checklist (Sutton *et al.* 1972) listed 31 native or naturalized species. Since then, the survey has added 4 species which are regarded as being native. Descriptions of these species are available only in the original species descriptions in journals or in foreign keys to species. It was therefore decided to bring together figures and brief descriptions of these 4 species in the present volume to provide a supplement to the existing works on the identification of woodlice in the British Isles (Edney 1953, 1954; Sutton *et al.* 1972; Sutton 1980).

FAMILY Trichoniscidae

Buddelundiella cataractae Verhoeff 1930

Buddelundiella cataractae rarely exceeds 3 mm in length and varies in colour from white to buff. The head is small with smooth-edged rounded lateral projections. Large longitudinal projections on the head are arranged thus: 2 centrally, 3 lower ridges close together on either side, and a single projection laterally on which the small eyes are situated. Each eye consists of 3 small black ocelli. The pereonites bear large rounded longitudinal ridges which each bear small spines on the apices. The number of ridges on the pereonites decreases posteriorly: 10-8-8-6-6-6-4. Pereonites II–IV have strongly narrowed lateral edges and a single deep furrow on the inner edge of the outer tubercle. These structures are probably related to the species' ability to roll into a ball shape.

The outline at the pereon-pleon junction is continuous and pleonite II bears 2 pairs of low rounded projections. This latter feature is sufficient to separate *B. cataractae* from other European species of the genus. The male pleopods are distinctive, especially the expanded and ridged tips of endopod I.

B. cataractae was re-described from British material by Oliver (1983).

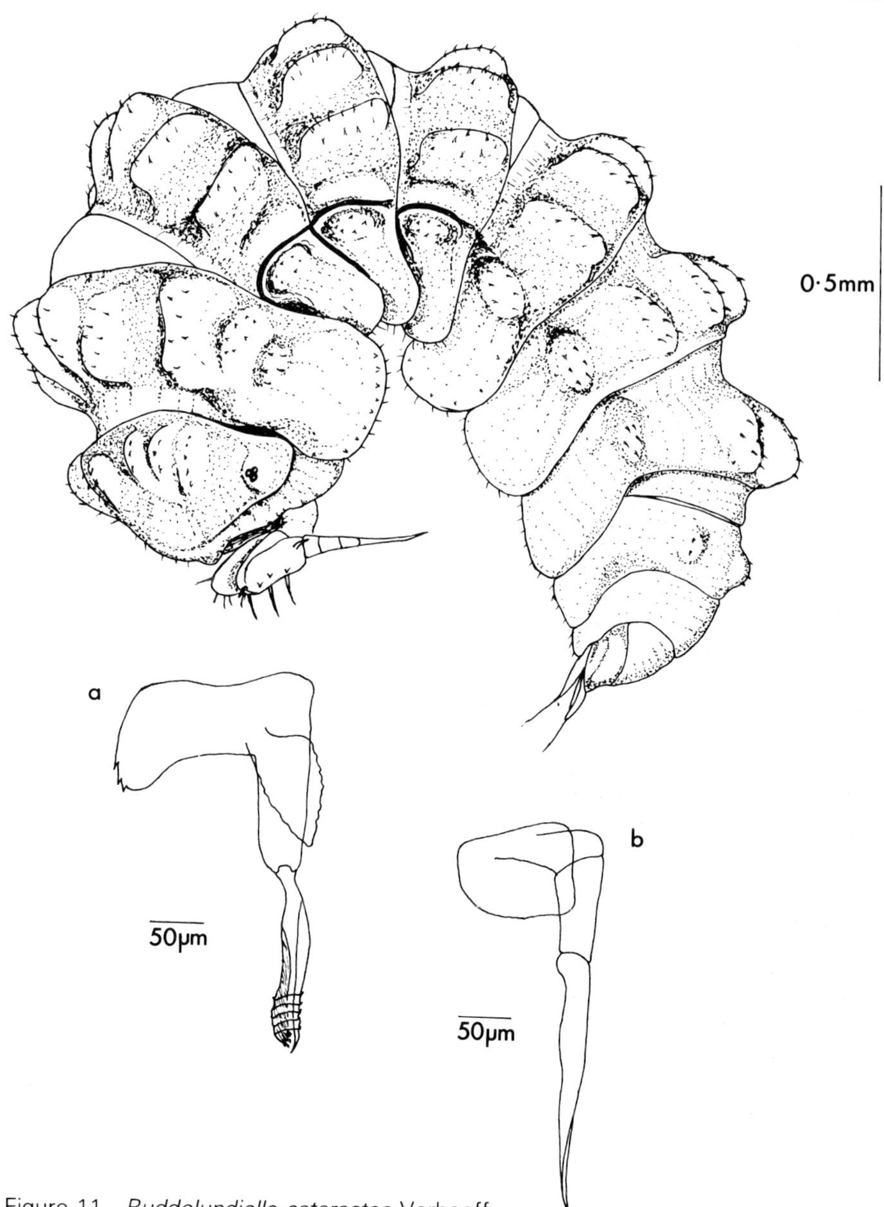

Figure 11 *Buddelundiella cataractae* Verhoeff

Lateral view of ♀ from Cardiff, Glamorgan

a. 1st ♂ pleopod
b. 2nd ♂ pleopod

FAMILY Trichoniscidae

Metatrichoniscoides celticus Oliver & Trew 1981

Metatrichoniscoides celticus is a small species (to 3 mm) with a narrow elongate outline. It is colourless in life except for white/yellowish-white subcuticular patches along the midline and over the pleon. The gut gives a central darker stripe. In alcohol the colour is uniformly white.

The head bears prominent lateral lobes which are squared with short spined tubercles at their corners. The top of the head is coarsely tuberculate, each tubercle bears a short spine. Eyes are absent.

The pereonites bear 2 rows of spined tubercles which decrease in prominence posteriorly. The pleon bears a row of very small spines on pleonites I–III but under low magnification appears smooth. The male pleopods are distinctive, especially the endopod of the 2nd pleopod which is greatly expanded and bears a prominent double-hooked tip. The tip of the endopod of the 1st pleopod is characterized by the brush-like setae from the swollen tip.

A complete description of *M. celticus* was given by Oliver and Trew (1981).

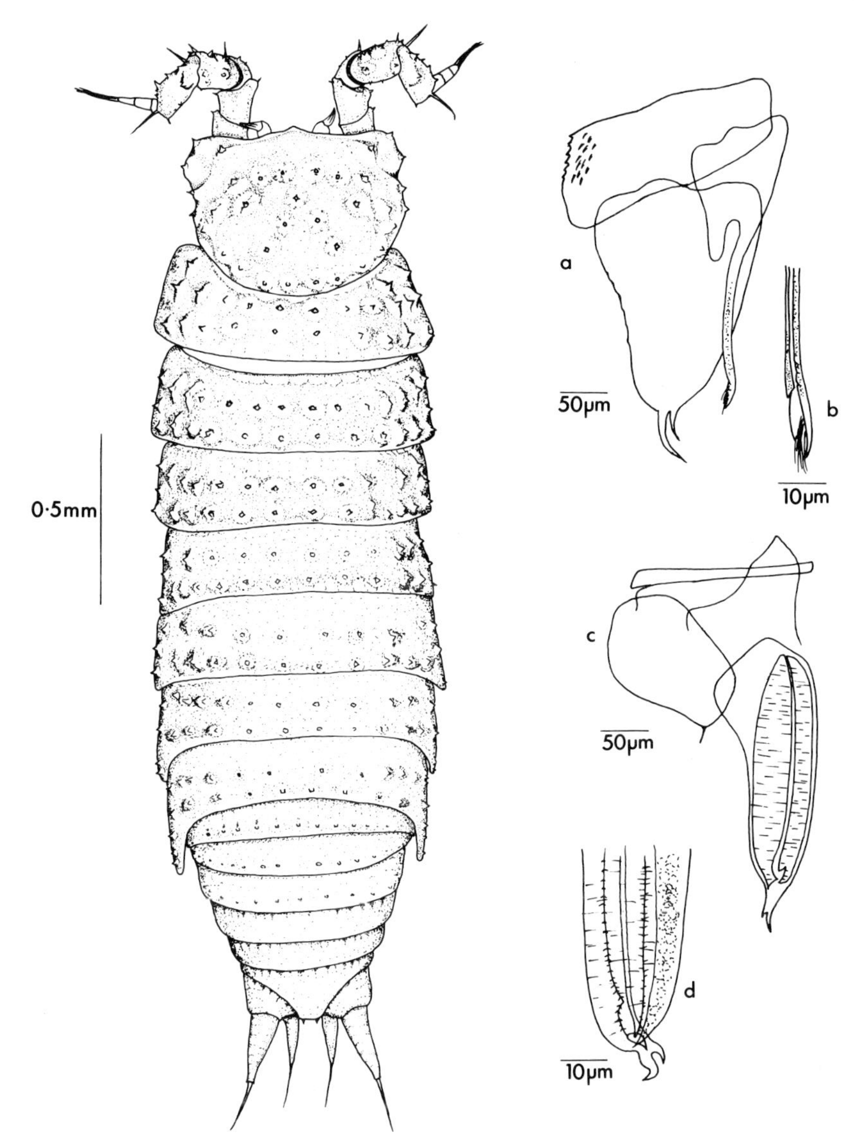

Figure 12 *Metatrichoniscoides celticus* Oliver & Trew

Dorsal view of ♀ from Nash Pt, Glamorgan

a. 1st ♂ pleopod
b. tip of endopod of 1st ♂ pleopod
c. 2nd ♂ pleopod
d. tip of endopod of 2nd ♂ pleopod

FAMILY Trichoniscidae

Miktoniscus patiencei Vandel 1946

Miktoniscus patiencei is small, rarely exceeding 4 mm in length. It is white in colour with the gut showing through the cuticle as a darker central stripe.

The head bears prominent, rounded, lateral lobes which are strongly tuberculate; the surface of the head is similarly tuberculate and the tubercles each bear a blunt peg. The eyes are composed of single large ocelli and are black in colour.

The pereonites are all coarsely tuberculate, with 4 irregular rows on the 1st pereonite and 3 irregular rows on pereonites II–VII. Pleonites I–III bear a single row of small tubercles and pleonites IV–V a single row of small spines.

The male pleopods are distinctive, the most striking feature being the tips of the endopods. The tip of endopod I is strongly serrated and that of endopod II tapered to a long fine point.

M. patiencei was re-described from British Isles material by Oliver and Sutton (1982).

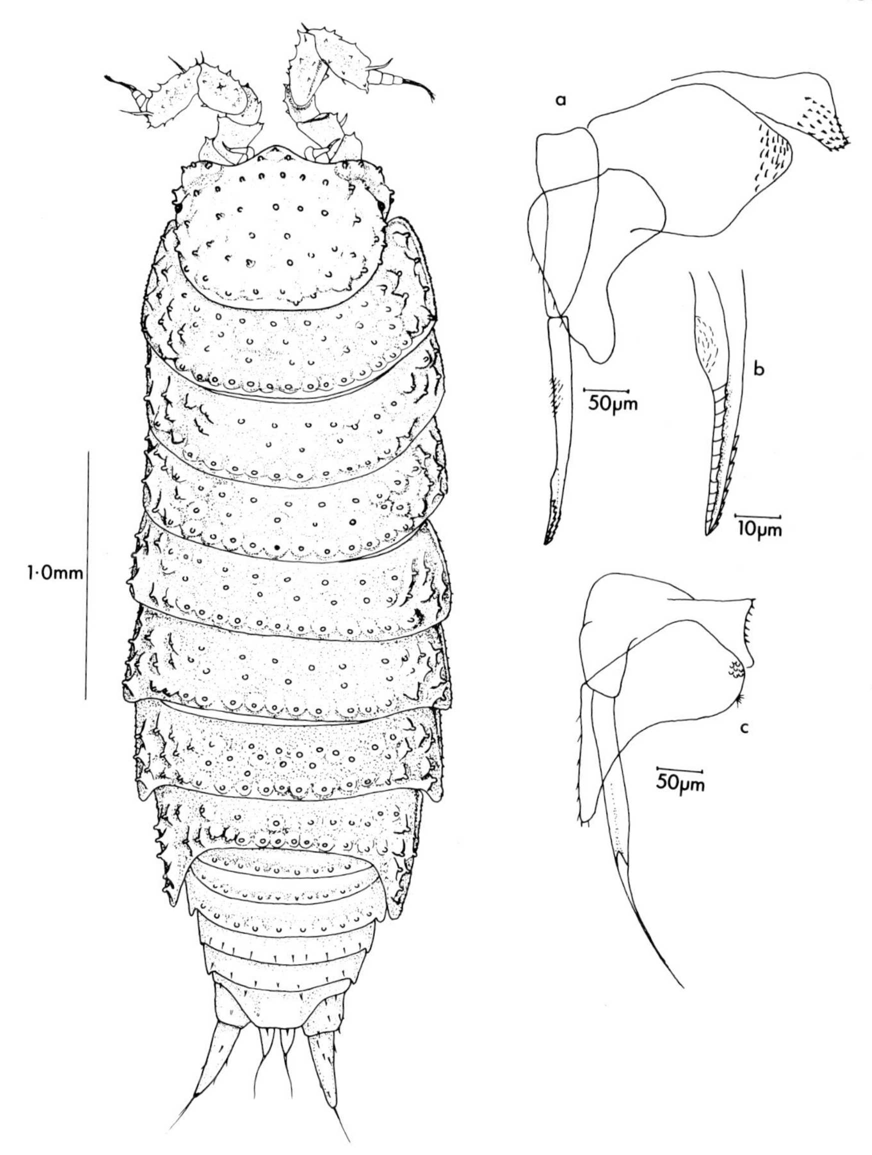

Figure 13 *Miktoniscus patiencei* Vandel

Dorsal view of ♀ from Isle of Wight

a. 1st ♂ pleopod
b. tip of endopod of 1st ♂ pleopod
c. 2nd ♂ pleopod

FAMILY Halophiloscidae

Stenophiloscia zosterae Verhoeff 1928

Stenophiloscia zosterae rarely exceeds 5.5 mm in length. It is pallid with a faint brownish colouration. The outline is rather elongate but the pleon–pereon junction is very distinct.

The head bears rounded lateral projections and has numerous small sharp spined tubercles on the dorsal surface. The eyes consist of few (<8) ocelli but are nevertheless prominent. The antennae are long with numerous, long, pointed spines; the flagellum consists of 3 sections.

The pereonites bear numerous small tubercles with pointed spines which show little pattern in their distribution but are roughly arranged in 4–6 'rows'. The pleonites bear spined tubercles on segments I–III. The telson is rounded posteriorly, with small spines. The uropods are lanceolate, ridged longitudinally and with an array of short setae.

The diagnostic characters of males include the 1st pereopod which bears a distinctive pattern of spines and areas of broad-tipped setae. The male genitalia of *S. zosterae* are distinguished from those of *H. couchi* by the shape of the tip of the 1st endopod and by the 2nd endopod which bears only a single spine on its inner edge.

S. zosterae has not previously been described or figured from British material.

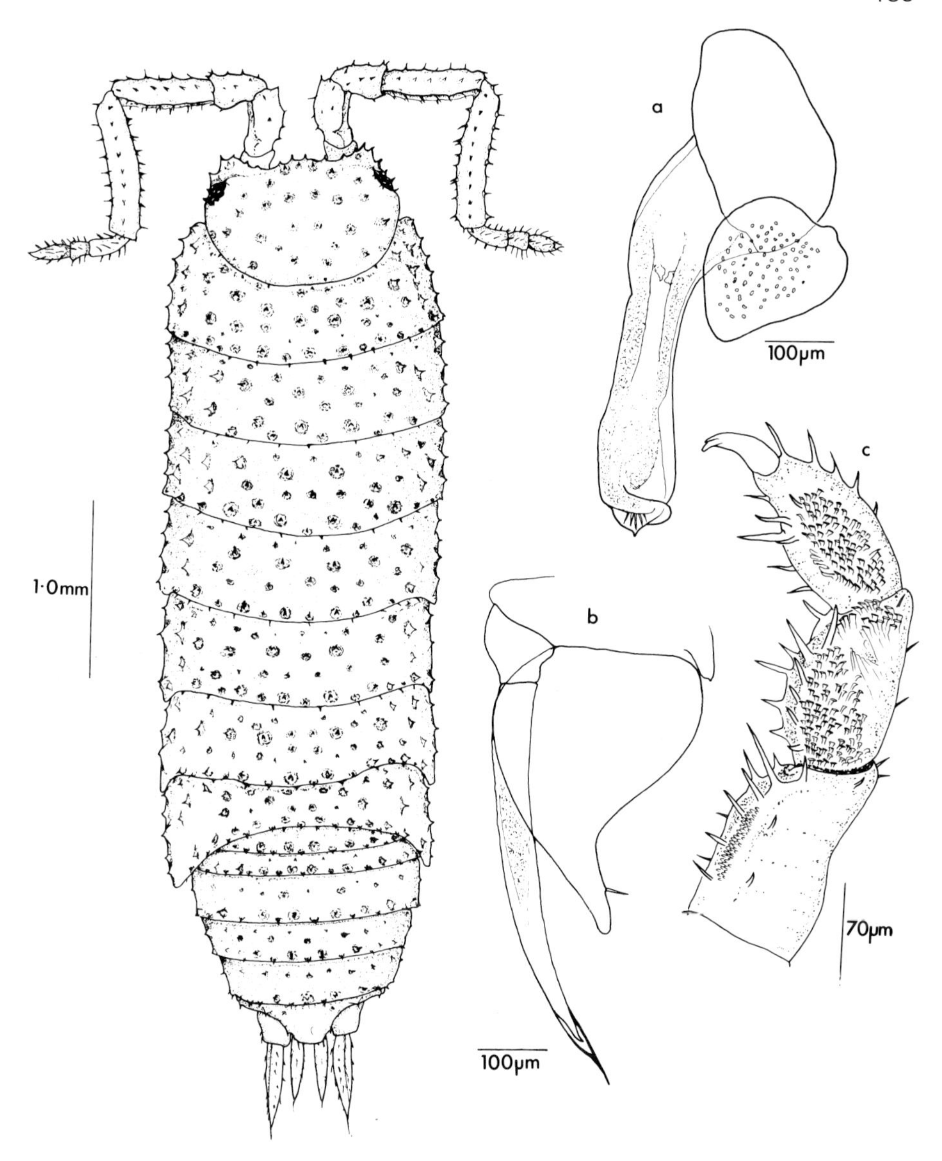

Figure 14 *Stenophiloscia zosterae* Verhoeff

Dorsal view of ♀ from Slapton Ley, Devon

a. 1st ♂ pleopod
b. 2nd ♂ pleopod
c. 1st ♂ pereopod, internal face

APPENDIX 3

TRACHELIPUS RATZEBURGI (Brandt)

Trachelipus ratzeburgi was first recorded from Britain (as *Porcellio ratzeburgi*) by Webb (1899), based on specimens from Warley, South Essex, identified by A M Norman. The species was figured and described by Webb and Sillem (1906) and thereafter was recorded widely in Britain (Collinge 1918b, 1943b; Taylor 1932, 1936, 1938; Ellis 1943), and once in Ireland (Collinge 1944b).

Specimens to support many of these published records have been examined by P T Harding in recent years, including material in the W E Collinge collection at the Yorkshire Museum (Harding 1977), the British Museum (Natural History), the National Museum of Ireland and in the private collection of Mr Ernest Taylor. The original specimens collected by Webb in Essex have not been traced.

The evidence from the specimens examined suggests that records, subsequent to Webb's discovery of the species in Essex, have been based on material identified using the figures and description given by Webb and Sillem (1906) and without reference to continental specimens. Whether Norman's original identification of Webb's specimen was correct must be a matter for conjecture. No specimens which in any way resemble *T. ratzeburgi* (Brandt) have been found among collections of British material; all specimens purporting to be this species have been *Porcellio* spp., *Trachelipus rathkei* (Brandt) or *Oniscus asellus* (L.). The only Irish specimens were, in fact, *Porcellio scaber*.

T. ratzeburgi is a distinctive species with very pronounced head lobes, quite unlike any other similar-sized species occurring in the British Isles. Its distribution in western Europe is centred on the Alps where it is a characteristic species of high alpine pastures. It has been recorded from parts of north Germany, Sweden and Norway but is absent from Denmark, Netherlands, Belgium and all but the extreme eastern departments of France.

All the above facts combine to provide a strong case for suggesting that *T. ratzeburgi* does not occur in the British Isles. For this reason, it has been omitted from the checklist on page 14.

APPENDIX 4

INSTRUCTIONS TO COLLECTORS

Isopod Survey Scheme **Myriapod Survey Scheme**

SURVEY OF MYRIAPODS AND NON-MARINE ISOPODS INSTRUCTIONS TO COLLECTORS

METHODS OF COLLECTING

1. Care should be taken to sample a wide variety of micro-habitats. It is tempting to concentrate on the undersides of stones and rotting logs, but this gives a very unbalanced idea of distribution.
2. Since these animals are nocturnal, collections made at dusk or later are of great value.
3. The use of baits is not advised as these may attract animals into areas they would not normally enter.
4. Soil species should not be neglected (for collecting these see Sutton 1972) *
5. Useful implements for collecting woodlice and myriapods include; (a) a 'widger' or metal prodder for parting soil and rotting wood; (b) a 'pooter' or bug sucker; and (c) (for picking up small animals) a camel hair brush moistened with alcohol.
6. Specimens should be as intact as possible Any parts that are shed should be kept with the specimen.
7. Adult males are essential for the identification of some isopods, and should be included in collections.
8. When searching for littoral myriapods, look as far as mid-tide level.

METHODS OF PRESERVING

Isopods are best preserved in 70% alcohol, myriapods in 70% alcohol with a little glycerine added. Material kept dry in the manner of insects is usually useless. Data labels written in pencil or indian ink should be kept with the specimens.

IDENTIFICATION

In view of the difficulty of identifying many specimens without experience or a reference collection, and because the scheme stands or falls on the reliability of identifications, recorders may be asked to send in specimens of all species so that the identification can be checked. We hope that recorders will appreciate that this is a necessary precaution at this stage of the project. Identified specimens will be returned on request so that each recorder can establish his own collection. We shall be pleased to help individuals or establishments wishing only to have material identified, provided that reasonable data are supplied.

SENDING MATERIAL AND CARDS BY POST

Specimens may be sent in alcohol in plastic or glass tubes well wrapped in cotton wool and boxed (e.g. in 2" x 2" colour transparancy boxes). Alternatively, since these animals live quite well in airtight tubes containing damp moss, they may be sent alive if first class mail is used. In all cases it is, of course, essential that each specimen tube is labelled in such a way that it can be identified with the correct record card.

In order not to cause damage, *PLEASE DO NOT FOLD THE CARDS FOR POSTING.*

* SUTTON S.L. 1972, 'Woodlice', pp. 144, Ginn & Co, London.

NOTES ON FILLING IN THE RECORD CARD

Please note that a NEW CARD should be used for *each* locality, *each* microsite and *each* date of collecting (or *each* time of collecting). If two or more species occur in the same microsite, they should appear on the *same* card.

GENERAL:

Grid references – should be given in the form 43/274/923 rather than SK/274/923; i.e. the 100 km. grid numbers rather than letters should be used. A minimum of *four* figures is necessary to define a 10 km. square, which is the basic unit of the survey. Hence, for the above location, the minimum grid reference that can be used would be 43/2 - - /9 - - . Advice on how to give a map reference is available on request, and is given at the bottom of 1" ordnance survey maps.

Locality – as precise as possible, at least to the nearest point mentioned in 1/4" O.S. map.

Recorder – name not initials.

Date – day, month, year.

V.C. and V.C. number – if in doubt, leave blank, but put name of county in locality box.

Altitude – to nearest 200 ft. (The 1/4" O.S. map uses coloured altitude symbols in units of 200 ft.)

Please do not write in the hatched areas.
Numbers printed on the cards are for computer purposes, please do not obscure these.

SPECIES LIST:

Several alien species not listed in Edney's key have been included, but ***Androniscus weberi*** (a synonym of ***A. dentiger***) and ***Armadillidum opacum*** (a doubtful record) have been omitted.

HABITAT DATA:

Starting with the major habitats, and working systematically through the card, complete this part *USING ONE TICK ONLY* in each section. Double ticking renders the card useless for computer analysis. If in doubt, leave a section blank.

N.B. Space does not allow a full coverage of aquatic habitats, but it is hoped that the recorder will use the 'Other Information' space, noting e.g. the size of the water body; and recording the age and character of the water body (e.g. Moat, Upland Tarn, Kettle Hole, Reservoir, Filter Bed.)

SECTION A

Coastal – 15 km. equals 9.5 miles

SECTION B – this is simply aimed at finding out the kind of neighbourhood in which the record was made.

SECTION C – all entries apply to the nature of the general area in which the record was made.

Lake – lake area is difficult to measure. As a guide, a round lake 0.4 hectare (=1 acre) in area will be about 50 yards in diameter.

Estuary – in this context means brackish water.

Marsh: Fen – marsh with neutral or alkaline pH;
Carr – marsh with a closed canopy of trees or scrub, usually alder;
Bog – acid marshland with ***Sphagnum*** growing on peat.

Cave, &c. – treated together because the environmental conditions are much the same in each.

Building – further details may be given in Section F.

Garden – public parks with flower beds, lawns, &c. should be included here, as should closely mown playing fields. Wilder parks come under grassland or woodland. Domestic garden is specified to make the distinction with Market Gardens, which come under 'Arable'.

Waste ground – includes derelict land in urban and rural situations, and such areas as car parks.

Grassland – the grazing pressure referred to here is the general pressure over the whole field. If animals are found in an isolated tussock in a heavily grazed field, 'Heavily grazed' should be ticked here, and 'Tussocks' ticked in Section E. Trampling in such places as public parks can be treated as grazing. 'Mown' includes hayfields and most motorway verges, but not close mown playing fields (q.v.)

Scrubland – woody plants of under 5 m. (=16 ft.).

Woodland: Dense – includes where herbs like Dog's Mercury and bluebells occur under closed canopy woodland;

Open with shrub – brambles count as scrub in this context.

Sand dune: Bare sand – should only be ticked where the area is extensive, e.g. a large blow-out. Bare sand of small blow-outs will come under 'Tussocky';

Tussocky – marram only;

Dense sward – mixed grasses including marram with herbs and prostrate woody plants;

Dune heath – low or prostrate vegetation (often moss/lichen) on stable dune slopes;

Other – if nothing in Section C is appropriate, tick here and specify the habitat in 'Other information'.

SECTION D – these are minor habitats that occur within the larger units in the last section. For 'Rockery', 'Dry stone wall', 'Quarry', &c., specify type of rock in Section H(d).

Hedge – includes small isolated area of scrub.

Embankment/cutting – includes steep gulleys caused by streams.

Grike – a crack in rock pavement of limestone, wide and deep enough to shelter plant life.

Dry ditch – with a very damp bed, but no standing water.

Wet ditch – a ditch with standing water.

Stabilised scree – overgrown with plants so that the stones are fixed in position.

Flood patch – areas liable to flooding in wet weather, e.g. corners of fields.

Vegetated stream – give details in 'Other information' of whether sample was from submerged or floating vegetation, and % cover.

Puddle – normally very small and impermanent.

Pond – can be very small, but is permanent.

SECTION E – enter here the actual microsite in which the animals found. The term Microsite is used instead of Microhabitat so as not to beg the question of whether a site *is* actually a Microhabitat, – the kind of place in which the animal normally occurs.

Litter – includes *any* type of litter (e.g. grass litter), except where the litter occurs within a well-defined tussock.

SECTION F – qualifying information about habitats already ticked.

Inhabited/public – will normally have some heating in winter, allowing sensitive species to survive.

Greenhouse (heated) – one free from frost in winter (if tropical, note in 'Other information').

Shore – 100 m. refers to the distance *above* high water mark for Spring tides.

Pleurococcoids – the single-celled algae responsible for the green colour on many tree trunks. Some woodlice graze on this growth.

Watercourse bed – specify general nature, which may be different from the microsite in which animals found.

SECTION G

Light level – this is light level experienced by the observer where he is collecting (usually the outside light, except in a cave or cellar).

SECTION H – applicable where collecting is taking place actually in the soil or litter, or in microsites closely associated with these, e.g. a rotting log.

Litter mainly – decisions about litter composition are always difficult to make. Only if one type is clearly dominant should it be ticked: otherwise indicate 'Mixed deciduous' or 'Mixed deciduous/coniferous', as appropriate. Sedge and grasses should only be ticked if positively identified as per the card: otherwise tick 'Grass – species unknown'.

Litter age: Both – tick where animals are distributed both in new, whole leaves above, and decomposed leaves below.

Litter cover – only applicable to woodland or scrub litter.

Humus type: Mull – soil/litter profiles with a crumbly texture, ill-defined transition between litter and soil layers and a good earthworm fauna. Neutral or alkaline pH.

Mor – profiles which are compacted, with few air spaces, and the transition between litter and soil layers is well-defined. Poor earthworm fauna: often rather acid.

N.B. Many soils cannot be fitted to either category, and cannot be ticked here.

SECTION I – gives information about the position of animals when found.

OTHER INFORMATION – this should be used whenever possible to fill-out the habitat description and to describe behaviour. Some points to comment upon are suggested.

CRITICISM – comments on difficulties encountered in filling-out the card will be appreciated.

Record cards and specimens should be sent to the under-named, from whom further information can be obtained:–

APPENDIX 5

RECORDS FROM HABITATS—OVERALL TOTALS

The following list gives the number of individual species records received for each habitat feature on the record card (see Figure 2). For each feature, the number of records is also expressed as a percentage of the total number of records for the section. The list follows the sequence of the card but omits the purely freshwater features (Section F (d) Waterspeed and F (e) Water-course bed) in which only the freshwater isopod genus *Asellus* was recorded.

The list of habitat records is followed by a list of the number and percentage of records received in each calendar month. All other totals of basic information (number of records, number of 10 km squares recorded, number of records with habitat data, etc) are given on page 31).

Habitat	No. of records	% of total
A Total number of records	23 478	
Coastal less than 15 km from sea	9 943	42.35
Inland more than 15 km from sea	13 535	57.65
B Total number of records	2 444	
Urban	1 249	5.33
Suburban/village	4 400	18.77
Rural	17 795	75.90
C IST ORDER HABITATS Total number of records	23 499	
Aquatic:		
Canal	10	0.04
River more than 5 m wide	15	0.06
Lake more than 1 acre (0.4 hectare)	74	0.31
Estuary	282	1.20
Sea	1 456	6.20
Marsh:		
Fen	203	0.86
Carr	151	0.64
Bog	67	0.29
Salt marsh	226	0.96
Cave/Well/Tunnel:		
Threshold	39	0.17
Dark zone	24	0.10
Building:		
Inside	332	1.41
Outside	1 263	5.37
Garden: Domestic	2 323	9.89

Habitat	No. of records	% of total
Waste ground:		
Less than 25% vegetation cover	1 220	5.19
More than 25% vegetation cover	2 368	10.08
Arable:		
Cereal crops	439	1.87
Root crops	18	0.08
Fodder crops	20	0.08
Grass ley	91	0.39
Market garden/Allotment	44	0.19
Grassland:		
Ungrazed	2 297	9.77
Lightly grazed	2 065	8.79
Heavily grazed	776	3.30
Mown	392	1.67
Scrubland:		
Dense	180	0.77
Open with herbs/grass	998	4.25
Woodland:		
Dense	1 032	4.39
Open with scrub	1 204	5.12
Open with herbs/grass	2 382	10.14
Acid heath/moor:		
Moss/lichen	24	0.10
Grass/sedge/rush	200	0.85
Heather	125	0.53
Vaccinium (bilberry)	0	—
Mixed	162	0.69
Sand dune:		
Bare sand	100	0.43
Tussocky	149	0.63
Dense sward	195	0.83
Dune slack	83	0.35
Dune heath	56	0.24
Other	414	1.76

D 2ND ORDER HABITATS Total number of records	13 036	
Cold frame	23	0.18
Rockery	303	2.32
Flower bed	282	2.16
Lawn	170	1.30
Compost/refuse heap	575	4.41
Dungheap	106	0.81
Hay (or other) stack	39	0.30
Potato (or other) clamp	0	—
Hedge	628	4.82
Roadside verge	2 493	19.12
Embankment/cutting	812	6.23
Woodland ride/firebreak	265	2.03
Wood fence	22	0.17
Dry stone wall	663	5.09

Habitat	No. of records	% of total
Wall with mortar	987	7.57
Quarry face	81	0.62
Quarry floor	802	6.15
Natural cliff face	887	6.80
Rock pavement	157	1.20
Stabilised scree	535	4.10
Unstabilised scree	176	1.35
Grike	12	0.09
Road/path	515	3.95
Dry watercourse bed	71	0.55
Dry ditch	185	1.42
Wet ditch	108	0.83
Shore/water edge/strandline	2 054	15.76
Vegetated stream	23	0.18
Unvegetated stream	8	0.06
Puddle	0	—
Pond less than 1 acre (0.4 hectare)	16	0.12
Flood patch	38	0.29
E MICROSITE Total number of records	23 246	
Stones	9 220	39.66
Shingle	267	1.15
Soil/sand	684	2.94
Litter	2 837	12.20
Tussocks	870	3.74
Bark (living trees or shrubs)	145	0.62
Dead wood	4 300	18.50
Dung	108	0.46
Carrion	2	0.01
Bracket fungi	9	0.04
Ant colony	409	1.76
Bird/mammal nest	44	0.19
Rock	664	2.86
Stone or brickwork	1 489	6.40
Shoreline jetsam	335	1.44
Human rubbish/garbage	1 083	4.66
Other	780	3.36
F HABITAT QUALIFIERS		
(a) Building: Total number of records	1 354	
Cellar	11	0.81
Inhabited/public	260	19.20
Uninhabited/outbuilding	307	22.67
Ruin	679	50.15
Greenhouse (heated)	53	3.91
Greenhouse (unheated)	44	3.25
(b) Shore: Total number of records	3 245	
Intertidal	367	11.31
Splash zone	1 187	36.58
Between splash zone and 100 m	1 383	42.62
100–1000m above HWM	308	9.49

Habitat	No. of records	% of total
(c) Encrustations: Total number of records	1 048	
Moss	809	77.20
Lichen	189	18.03
Pleurococcoids	50	4.77
G LIGHT LEVEL Total number of records	23 029	
Full daylight	21 580	93.71
Half light/dusk/dawn	956	4.15
Dark	493	2.14
H SOIL/LITTER DETAILS		
(a) Total number of records	8 128	
Litter mainly:		
Oak	552	6.79
Beech	496	6.10
Birch	93	1.14
Sycamore	119	1.46
Mixed deciduous	1 448	17.82
Coniferous	142	1.75
Mixed deciduous/coniferous	237	2.92
Gorse	12	0.15
Hawthorn	138	1.70
Heathers	73	0.90
Sea buckthorn	0	—
Litter/vegetation mainly:		
Carex	56	0.69
Molinia	16	0.20
Dactylis	51	0.63
Festuca	192	2.36
Bromus	8	0.10
Brachypodium	70	0.86
Grass—species unknown	1 421	17.48
Mixed grass/herbs	1 900	23.38
Nettles	77	0.95
Reeds (*Phragmites*)	75	0.92
Juncus	42	0.52
Bracken	62	0.76
Other	848	10.43
(b) Litter age: Total number of records	4 500	
Fresh	562	12.49
Old	1 342	29.82
Both	2 596	57.69
(c) Litter cover: Total number of records	3 438	
Exposed	1 100	32.00
Protected by thin vegetation	1 370	39.85
Protected by thick vegetation	968	28.15
(d) Soil/exposed rock: Total number of records	9 331	
Calcareous	4 979	53.36
Non-calcareous	4 352	46.64

Habitat	No. of records	% of total
(e) Soil: Total number of records	8548	
Heavy clay	255	2.98
Clayey	2119	24.79
Peat	514	6.01
Loam	3528	41.27
Sandy	1871	21.89
Pure sand	261	3.05
(f) Humus type: Total number of records	1772	
Mull	1446	81.60
Mor	326	18.40
I LOCATION OF ANIMAL		
(a) Horizon: Total number of records	16326	
More than 3 m above ground	115	0.70
Less than 3 m above ground	1998	12.24
On ground surface	10029	61.43
In litter	2898	17.75
Less than 10 cm in soil	1161	7.11
More than 10 cm in soil	125	0.77
(b) Position: Total number of records	5439	
In open	634	11.66
In crevice	4805	88.34

NUMBER AND PERCENTAGE OF RECORDS IN EACH MONTH

Total number of records	26155	
January	370	1.41%
February	768	2.94%
March	1473	5.63%
April	2533	9.68%
May	2994	11.45%
June	3754	14.35%
July	3373	12.90%
August	3379	12.92%
September	3563	13.62%
October	2411	9.22%
November	916	3.50%
December	621	2.37%

APPENDIX 6

RED DATA LISTS

The following lists include species which, in our opinion, are or have been threatened in Great Britain and in Ireland. The 6 threat categories are basically those developed for the *British red data books: 2. Insects* (Shirt 1985), following the example of *The IUCN invertebrate red data book* (Wells, Pyle & Collins 1983), with some small amendments. The 6 threat categories are as follows.

1. *Endangered*
   Taxa in danger of extinction and whose survival is unlikely if the causal factors continue operating.
2. *Vulnerable*
   Taxa believed likely to move into the endangered category in the near future, if the causal factors continue operating.
3. *Rare*
   Taxa with small populations that are not at present endangered or vulnerable, but are at risk.
4. *Out of danger*
   Taxa formerly included in one of the above categories, but which are now considered relatively secure.
5. *Endemic*
   Taxa which are native to, and restricted to, a particular geographical region. (Taxa within this category may also be in any of categories 1–4.)
6. *Extinct*
   Taxa not definitely located in the wild during the past 50 years.

Separate lists for Great Britain and for Ireland are included. The 2 political units in Ireland have not been separated.

GREAT BRITAIN

Categories 2 (Vulnerable) and 5 (Endemic) METATRICHONISCOIDES CELTICUS
Known only from 7 sites along the coasts of the administrative counties of South and Mid Glamorgan. The habitat described by Oliver and Trew (1981) suggests that *M. celticus* may be vulnerable to marine pollution, human disturbance and the development of sites.

Category 3 (Rare) ARMADILLIDIUM ALBUM
Recorded from the beaches or salt marshes of several dune systems and estuaries. Many sites are protected as National Nature Reserves or Sites of

Special Scientific Interest. The species is believed to be adversely affected by disturbance of drift lines by man.

Category 3 (Rare) ARMADILLIDIUM PICTUM
Known from a few isolated sites in western Britain. Most of the sites are small and surrounded by unfavourable habitat.

Category 4 (Out of danger) HALOPHILOSCIA COUCHI
This species was formerly considered to be uncommon so that a special survey was made to define its habitat. A grant from the World Wildlife Fund (British National Appeal) supported a survey of sites in Devon and Cornwall in 1973 (Harding 1973, 1975) which provided detailed knowledge of the species' habitat. Subsequent records of *H. couchi* suggest that it is sufficiently widespread to be considered out of danger.

IRELAND

Category 2 (Vulnerable) TRICHONISCOIDES ALBIDUS
Known from only 2 localities, both of which are very vulnerable to modification. One site at The Strawberry Beds, near Lucan, Dublin, is also a site for *Trichoniscoides sarsi* (see below) and the rare millipede *Stygioglomeris crinita* Brolemann.

Category 2 (Vulnerable) TRICHONISCOIDES SARSI
Recorded at only 3 localities, all of which are vulnerable to development or modification. The precise habitat requirements of this species are poorly understood but, on present evidence, it is restricted to small areas of calcareous soils. One site, The Strawberry Beds, is important for other rare species (see *Trichoniscoides albidus*).

Category 3 (Rare) HALOPHILOSCIA COUCHI
Known from Howth, Dublin, but recorded only once in the last 50 years. Doogue and Harding (1982) considered that it was probably not limited to Howth, but on present information the species is clearly vulnerable, at Howth, to marine pollution.

Category 3 (Rare) ARMADILLIDIUM ALBUM
Recorded from several east coast beach and dune complexes. This species is believed to be adversely affected by disturbance of drift lines by man, and the removal of sand from beaches and dune systems.

Category 6 (Extinct) ACAEROPLASTES MELANURUS
Known from Howth, Dublin, but apparently not recorded since 1934.

NOTES